Hymns and songs for assembly

kevin
mayhew

First published in Great Britain in 2002 by KEVIN MAYHEW LIMITED
Buxhall, Stowmarket, Suffolk IP14 3BW E-mail info@kevinmayhewltd.com

Compilation © Kevin Mayhew Ltd 2002

4 5 6 7 8 9

Catalogue No. 1413191
ISBN No. 1 84003 929 9
ISMN No. M 57024 091 3

Cover design by Angela Selfe Typesetting by Louise Selfe
Printed in Great Britain

General hymns and songs

1 Dave Bilbrough

Abba, Father, let me be
yours and yours alone.
May my will for ever be
more and more your own.
Never let my heart grow cold,
never let me go.
Abba, Father, let me be
yours and yours alone.

2 William Henry Draper, alt.

All creatures of our God and King,
lift up your voice and with us sing,
O praise him, alleluia!
Thou burning sun with golden beam,
thou silver moon with softer gleam,

O praise him, O praise him,
alleluia, alleluia, alleluia.

Let all things their Creator bless,
and worship him in humbleness,
O praise him, alleluia!
Praise, praise the Father, praise the Son,
and praise the Spirit, Three in One.

3 Donald Fishel

Alleluia, alleluia,
give thanks to the risen Lord,
alleluia, alleluia,
give praise to his name.

Jesus is Lord of all the earth,
he is the King of creation.

Spread the good news o'er all the earth,
Jesus has died and has risen.

Come, let us praise the living God,
joyfully sing to our Saviour.

4 Roy Turner

All over the world the Spirit is moving,
all over the world,
as the prophets said it would be.
All over the world
there's a mighty revelation
of the glory of the Lord,
as the waters cover the sea.

All over this land the Spirit is moving,
all over this land,
as the prophets said it would be.
All over this land
there's a mighty revelation
of the glory of the Lord,
as the waters cover the sea.

All over the Church the Spirit is moving,
all over the Church,
as the prophets said it would be.
All over the Church
there's a mighty revelation
of the glory of the Lord,
as the waters cover the sea.

All over us all the Spirit is moving,
all over us all,
as the prophets said it would be.
All over us all
there's a mighty revelation
of the glory of the Lord,
as the waters cover the sea.

Continued overleaf

Deep down in my heart the Spirit is
    moving,
deep down in my heart,
as the prophets said it would be.
Deep down in my heart
there's a mighty revelation
of the glory of the Lord,
as the waters cover the sea.

5 adapted by Winifred E. Barnard

All the flowers are waking,
spring has come again;
God has sent the sunshine,
God has sent the rain.

All the trees are waking,
spring has come again;
God has sent the sunshine,
God has sent the rain.

All the birds are singing,
spring has come again;
singing in the sunshine,
singing in the rain.

A verse for winter

All the flowers are sleeping
underneath the ground;
sleeping in the winter,
sleeping safe and sound.

6 Cecil Frances Alexander

All things bright and beautiful,
all creatures great and small,
all things wise and wonderful,
the Lord God made them all.

Each little flow'r that opens,
each little bird that sings,
he made their glowing colours,
he made their tiny wings.

The purple-headed mountain,
the river running by,
the sunset and the morning
that brightens up the sky.

The cold wind in the winter,
the pleasant summer sun,
the ripe fruits in the garden,
he made them ev'ry one.

He gave us eyes to see them,
and lips that we might tell
how great is God almighty
who has made all things well.

7 Unknown

A new commandment
I give unto you:
that you love one another
as I have loved you,
that you love one another
as I have loved you.

By this shall all know
that you are my disciples,
if you have love one for another.
By this shall all know
that you are my disciples,
if you have love one for another.

8 Martin Nystrom

As the deer pants for the water,
so my soul longs after you.
You alone are my heart's desire
and I long to worship you.

You alone are my strength, my shield,
to you alone may my spirit yield.
You alone are my heart's desire
and I long to worship you.

I want you more than gold or silver,
only you can satisfy.
You alone are the real joy-giver
and the apple of my eye.

You're my friend and you're my brother,
even though you are a king.
I love you more than any other,
so much more than anything.

9 Estelle White

Autumn days when the grass is jewelled
    and the
silk inside a chestnut shell,
jet planes meeting in the air to get
    refuelled,
all these things I love so well.

So I mustn't forget.
No, I mustn't forget,
to say a great big thank you,
I mustn't forget.

Clouds that look like familiar faces,
    and a
winter's moon with frosted rings,
smell of bacon as I fasten up my laces,
and the song the milkman sings.

Whipped up spray that is rainbow-
    scattered, and a
swallow curving in the sky.
Shoes so comfy though they're worn-
    out and they're battered,
and the taste of apple pie.

Scent of gardens when the rain's
    been falling, and a
minnow darting down a stream,
picked-up engine that's been stuttering
    and stalling,
and a win for my home team.

10 Paul Field

A wiggly, waggly worm, a slipp'ry,
    slimy slug,
a creepy, crawly, buzzy thing, a tickly,
    wickly bug;
of all the things to be, I'm happy that
    I'm me.
Thank you, Lord, I'm happy that I'm me.
I'm happy that I'm me, happy that I'm
    me.
There's no one else in all the world
    that I would rather be.
A wiggly, waggly worm, a slippery,
    slimy slug,
a creepy, crawly, buzzy thing, a tickly,
    wickly bug.

Continued overleaf

A prickly porcupine, a clumsy kangaroo,
a croaky frog, a hairy hog, a monkey
    in a zoo;
of all the things to be, I'm happy that
    I'm me.
Thank you, Lord, I'm happy that I'm me.
I'm happy that I'm me, happy that I'm
    me.
There's no one else in all the world
    that I would rather be.
A prickly porcupine, a clumsy kangaroo,
a croaky frog, a hairy hog, a monkey
    in a zoo.

© 1991 Daybreak Music Ltd

11 Morris Chapman

Be bold, be strong,
for the Lord, your God, is with you.
Be bold, be strong,
for the Lord, your God, is with you.
I am not afraid, I am not dismayed,
because I'm walking in faith and victory,
come on and walk in faith and victory,
for the Lord, your God, is with you.

© 1983 Word Music/CopyCare Ltd

12 Unknown, based on Psalm 46

Be still and know that I am God. (3)

In you, O Lord, I put my trust. (3)

13 David J. Evans

Be still, for the presence of the Lord,
the Holy One, is here;
come, bow before him now
with reverence and fear.
In him no sin is found,
we stand on holy ground.
Be still, for the presence of the Lord,
the Holy One, is here.

Be still, for the glory of the Lord
is shining all around;
he burns with holy fire,
with splendour he is crowned.
How awesome is the sight,
our radiant King of light!
Be still, for the glory of the Lord
is shining all around.

Be still, for the power of the Lord
is moving in this place;
he comes to cleanse and heal,
to minister his grace.
No work too hard for him,
in faith receive from him.
Be still, for the power of the Lord
is moving in this place.

© 1986 Thankyou Music

14 Graham Kendrick

Big man standing by the blue waterside,
mending nets by the blue sea.
Along came Jesus, he said:
'Simon Peter, won't you leave your nets
    and come follow me.'

'You don't need anything,
  I've got ev'rything,
but Peter, it's gonna be a hard way.
You don't have to worry now, come
  on and hurry now,
I'll walk beside you ev'ry day.'

Life wasn't easy for the big fisherman,
but still he followed till his dying day.
Along came Jesus, he said,
'Simon Peter, there's a place in heaven
  where you can stay.'

15 Bob Gillman

Bind us together, Lord,
bind us together,
with cords that cannot be broken.
Bind us together, Lord,
bind us together, Lord,
bind us together in love.

There is only one God,
there is only one King.
There is only one Body,
that is why we sing:

Fit for the glory of God,
purchased by his precious Blood,
born with the right to be free:
Jesus the vict'ry has won.

We are the fam'ly of God,
we are his promise divine,
we are his chosen desire,
we are the glorious new wine.

16 Geoffrey Marshall-Taylor

Can you be sure that the rain will fall?
Can you be sure that birds will fly?
Can you be sure that rivers will flow?
Or that the sun will light the sky?

God has promised.
God never breaks a promise
  he makes.
His word is always true.

Can you be sure that the tide will turn?
Can you be sure that grass will grow?
Can you be sure that night will come,
Or that the sun will melt the snow?

You can be sure that God is near;
You can be sure he won't let you down;
You can be sure he'll always hear;
And that he's given Jesus, his Son.

17 Marion Payton

Carpenter, carpenter, make me a tree,
that's the work of somebody far
  greater than me;
gardener, gardener, shape me a flower,
that's the work of somebody with far
  greater power.

Somebody greater than you or me,
put the apple on the apple tree;
the flower in the earth and the fish
  in the sea,
are by somebody greater than you
  or me.

Continued overleaf

Builder, now raise up a coloured rainbow,
that's something far greater than people could know;
farmer, I ask you, design me some corn,
that's somebody greater than any man born.

Somebody greater than you or me,
put the apple on the apple tree;
the flower in the earth and the fish in the sea,
are by somebody greater than you or me.

Now, electrician, will you light a star,
that's the work of somebody who's greater by far;
plumber, connect up the river and sea,
that's the work of somebody far greater than me.

© Marion Payton (Skelton)

18 Sue McClellan, John Paculabo and Keith Ryecroft

Colours of day dawn into the mind,
the sun has come up, the night is behind.
Go down in the city, into the street,
and let's give the message to the people we meet.

So light up the fire and let the flame burn,
open the door, let Jesus return.
Take seeds of his Spirit,
let the fruit grow,
tell the people of Jesus,
let his love show.

Go through the park, on into the town;
the sun still shines on, it never goes down.
The light of the world is risen again;
the people of darkness are needing a friend.

Open your eyes, look into the sky,
the darkness has come, the sun came to die.
The evening draws on, the sun disappears,
but Jesus is living, his Spirit is near.

© 1974 Thankyou Music

19 Traditional (adapted)

Come and praise the Lord our King, hallelujah,
Come and praise the Lord our King, hallelujah.

Christ was born in Bethlehem, hallelujah,
Son of God and Son of Man, hallelujah.

From him love and wisdom came, hallelujah;
All his life was free from blame, hallelujah.

Jesus died at Calvary, hallelujah,
rose again triumphantly, hallelujah.

He will be with us today, hallelujah,
and forever with us stay, hallelujah.

20 Patricia Morgan

Come on and celebrate!
His gift of love we will celebrate –
the Son of God who loved us
and gave us life.
We'll shout your praise, O King:
you give us joy nothing else can bring;
we'll give to you our offering
in celebration praise.

Come on and celebrate,
celebrate, celebrate and sing,
celebrate and sing to the King!
Come on and celebrate,
celebrate, celebrate and sing,
celebrate and sing to the King!

21 Karen Lafferty

Don't build your house on the sandy
    land,
don't build it too near the shore.
Well, it might look kind of nice,
but you'll have to build it twice,
oh, you'll have to build your house
    once more.
You'd better * build your house upon
    a rock,
make a good foundation on a solid spot.
Oh, the storms may come and go
but the peace of God you will know.

*If sung as a round the second group
of voices enters here.*

22 Ian Smale

Father God, I wonder
how I managed to exist
without the knowledge of your
    parenthood
and your loving care.
But now I am your child,
I am adopted in your family
and I can never be alone
'cause, Father God, you're there
    beside me.

I will sing your praises,
I will sing your praises,
I will sing your praises,
for evermore.
I will sing your praises,
I will sing your praises,
I will sing your praises,
for evermore.

23 Jenny Hewer

Father, I place into your hands
the things that I can't do.
Father, I place into your hands
the times that I've been through.
Father, I place into your hands
the way that I should go,
for I know I always can trust you.

Father, I place into your hands
my friends and family.
Father, I place into your hands
the things that trouble me.
Father, I place into your hands
the person I would be,
for I know I always can trust you.

Continued overleaf

Father, we love to seek your face,
we love to hear your voice.
Father, we love to sing your praise,
and in your name rejoice.
Father, we love to walk with you,
and in your presence rest,
for we know we always can trust you.

Father, I want to be with you
and do the things you do.
Father, I want to speak the words
that you are speaking too.
Father, I want to love the ones
that you will draw to you,
for I know that I am one with you.

24 Terrye Coelho

Father, we adore you,
lay our lives before you.
How we love you!

Jesus, we adore you . . .

Spirit, we adore you . . .

25 Robin Mann

Father welcomes all his children
to his fam'ly through his Son.
Father giving his salvation,
life for ever has been won.

Little children, come to me,
for my kingdom is of these.
Love and new life have I to give,
pardon for your sin.

In the water, in the word,
in his promise, be assured:
all who believe and are baptised
shall be born again.

Let us daily die to sin;
let us daily rise with him –
walk in the love of Christ our Lord,
live in the peace of God.

26 Donna Adkins

Father, we love you,
we praise you, we adore you,
glorify your name in all the earth.
Glorify your name, glorify your name,
glorify your name in all the earth.

Jesus, we love you . . .

Spirit, we love you . . .

27 Michael Cockett

Follow me, follow me, leave your
 home and family,
leave your fishing nets and boats
 upon the shore.
Leave the seeds that you have sown,
leave the crops that you've grown,
leave the people you have known
 and follow me.

The foxes have their holes
and the swallows have their nests,
but the Son of Man
has no place to lay down.
I do not offer comfort,
I do not offer wealth,
but in me will true happiness be found.

If you would follow me,
you must leave old ways behind.
You must take my cross
and follow on my path.
You may be far from loved ones,
you may be far from home,
but my Father will welcome you at last.

Although I go away
you will never be alone,
for the Spirit will be there
to comfort you.
Though all of you may scatter,
each follow their own path,
still the Spirit of love will lead you home.

28 Graham Kendrick

From heav'n you came, helpless babe,
entered our world, your glory veiled;
not to be served but to serve,
and give your life that we might live.

This is our God, the Servant King,
he calls us now to follow him,
to bring our lives as a daily offering
of worship to the Servant King.

There in the garden of tears,
my heavy load he chose to bear;
his heart with sorrow was torn,
'Yet not my will, but yours,' he said.

Come, see his hands and his feet,
the scars that speak of sacrifice,
hands that flung stars into space
to cruel nails surrendered.

So let us learn how to serve,
and in our lives enthrone him;
each other's needs to prefer,
for it is Christ we're serving.

29 Jancis Harvey

From the darkness came light,
from the blackest of nights;
Wait for the morning, the sunlight,
*   the dawning;*
from the darkness came light.

Earth so dark and so cold, what great
   secrets you hold;
The promise of spring, the wonder
   you bring;
the beauty of nature unfolds.

Jesus was born in a stall, born to
   bring light to us all.
He came to love us, a new life to
   give us;
Jesus was born in a stall.

Jesus died on Calvary, suffered for you
   and me;
He rose from the dark and gloom,
   out of a stony tomb,
walked in the world and was free.

We have this new life to share, a love
   to pass on everywhere;
Time spent in giving, a joy in our living,
in showing to others we care.

30 Geoffrey Gardner

(1) From the tiny ant
(2) **From the tiny ant,**
(1) To the elephant,
(2) **To the elephant,**
(1) From the snake to the kangaroo,
(2) **From the snake to the kangaroo,**
(1) From the great white shark,
(2) **From the great white shark,**
(1) To the singing lark,
(2) **To the singing lark,**
(1) Care for them, it's up to you,
(2) **Care for them, it's up to you,**
(1 & 2) Care for them, it's up to you.
(1 & 2) Care for them, it's up to you.
(1 & 2) No one else will care for them,
(1) It's up,
(2) **It's up,**
(1 & 2) It's up to you.

(1) From the tabby cat,
(2) **From the tabby cat,**
(1) To the desert rat,
(2) **To the desert rat,**
(1) From the hamster to the
     chimpanzee,
(2) **From the hamster to the
     chimpanzee,**
(1) From the common tern,
(2) **From the common tern,**
(1) To the crawling worm,
(2) **To the crawling worm,**
(1) Care for them, it's up to me,
(2) **Care for them, it's up to me,**
(1 & 2) Care for them it's up to me.
(1 & 2) Care for them it's up to me.
(1 & 2) No one else will care for them,
(1) It's up,
(2) **It's up,**
(1 & 2) It's up to me.

(1) From the mongrel dog,
(2) **From the mongrel dog,**
(1) To the snorting hog,
(2) **To the snorting hog,**
(1) From the badger to the platypus,
(2) **From the badger to the platypus,**
(1) From the small minnow,
(2) **From the small minnow,**
(1) To the white rhino,
(2) **To the white rhino,**
(1) Care for them it's up to us,
(2) **Care for them it's up to us,**
(1 & 2) Care for them it's up to us.
(1 & 2) Care for them it's up to us.
(1 & 2) No one else will care for them,
(1) It's up,
(2) **It's up,**
(1 & 2) It's up to us.

Actions
At the end of each verse, use arms
to point at others (verse 1), to point
at yourselves (verse 2) and to wave
in the air (verse 3).

*This song can be sung by two groups,
indicated by (1) and (2). Generally,
group (2) echoes group (1), or everyone can sing every line.*

© Geoffrey Gardner

31 Traditional

Give me joy in my heart,
     keep me praising,
give me joy in my heart, I pray.
Give me joy in my heart,
     keep me praising,
keep me praising till the end of day.

Sing hosanna! Sing hosanna!
Sing hosanna to the King of kings!
Sing hosanna! Sing hosanna!
Sing hosanna to the King!

Give me peace in my heart,
   keep me resting . . .

Give me love in my heart,
   keep me serving . . .

Give me oil in my lamp,
   keep me burning . . .

32 Geoffrey Gardner

Give us hope, Lord, for each day,
give us hope, Lord, for each day,
guide our footsteps on the way,
give us hope, Lord, for each day.

Give us strength, Lord, for each day . . .

Give us peace, Lord, for each day . . .

Give us love, Lord, for each day . . .

Give us joy, Lord, for each day . . .

Alternative words

Give us friends, Lord, for each day,
give us friends, Lord, for each day,
make us thankful on the way,
give us friends, Lord, for each day.

Give us food, Lord, for each day . . .

Give us homes, Lord, for each day . . .

Give us clothes, Lord, for each day . . .

© Geoffrey Gardner

33 Carol Owens

God forgave my sin in Jesus' name.
I've been born again in Jesus' name;
and in Jesus' name I come to you
to share his love as he told me to.

> *He said, 'Freely, freely you have*
>   *received;*
> *freely, freely give.*
> *Go in my name, and because you*
>   *believe,*
> *others will know that I live.'*

All pow'r is giv'n in Jesus' name,
in earth and heav'n in Jesus' name;
and in Jesus' name I come to you
to share his pow'r as he told me to.

God gives us life in Jesus' name,
he lives in us in Jesus' name;
and in Jesus' name I come to you
to share his peace as he told me to.

© 1972 Bud John Songs/EMI Christian Music Publishing/CopyCare Ltd

34 Percy Dearmer (1867-1936) alt.

God is love: his the care,
tending each, ev'rywhere.
God is love, all is there!
Jesus came to show him,
that we all might know him!

> *Sing aloud, loud, loud!*
> *Sing aloud, loud, loud!*
> *God is good! God is truth!*
> *God is beauty! Praise him!*

Continued overleaf

None can see God above;
we can share life and love;
thus may we Godward move,
seek him in creation,
holding ev'ry nation.

> *Sing aloud, loud, loud!*
> *Sing aloud, loud, loud!*
> *God is good! God is truth!*
> *God is beauty! Praise him!*

Jesus lived on the earth,
hope and life brought to birth
and affirmed human worth,
for he came to save us
by the truth he gave us.

To our Lord praise we sing,
light and life, friend and King,
coming down, love to bring,
pattern for our duty,
showing God in beauty.

35 Peter Lewis

> *God made the colours of the rainbow,*
> *yellow, red and blue,*
> *God made the colours of the rainbow,*
> *just for me and you.*

God made the colours of the flowers,
purple, blue and red,
God made the colours of the flowers,
in our flowerbed.

God made the colours of our pictures,
orange, green and pink,
God made the colours of our pictures,
pencils, paint and ink.

God made the colours of the seasons,
golden, green and white,
God made the colours of the seasons,
changing with the light.

God made the colours of the weather,
yellow, blue and grey,
God made the colours of the weather,
different every day.

36 Alan Dale and Hubert J. Richards

God's Spirit is in my heart.
He has called me and set me apart.
This is what I have to do,
what I have to do.

> *He sent me to give the Good News*
> *to the poor*
> *tell pris'ners that they are pris'ners*
> *no more,*
> *tell blind people that they can see,*
> *and set the downtrodden free,*
> *and go tell everyone*
> *the news that the kingdom of God*
> *has come,*
> *and go tell everyone*
> *the news that God's kingdom has*
> *come.*

Just as the Father sent me,
so I'm sending you out to be
my witnesses throughout the world,
the whole of the world.

Don't carry a load in your pack,
you don't need two shirts on your back.
A workman can earn his own keep,
can earn his own keep.

Don't worry what you have to say,
don't worry because on that day
God's Spirit will speak in your heart,
will speak in your heart.

Nobody can live who hasn't any water,
when the land is dry, then nothing
  much grows;
Jesus gives us life if we drink the living
  water,
sing it so that ev'rybody knows.

37 Traditional

Halle, halle, hallelujah!
Halle, halle, hallelujah!
Halle, halle, hallelujah!
Hallelujah, hallelujah!

38 Christian Strover

Have you heard the raindrops drumming
  on the rooftops?
Have you heard the raindrops dripping
  on the ground?
Have you heard the raindrops splashing
  in the streams
and running to the rivers all around?

There's water, water of life,
Jesus gives us the water of life;
there's water, water of life,
Jesus gives us the water of life.

There's a busy worker digging in the
  desert,
digging with a spade that flashes in
  the sun;
soon there will be water rising in the
  well-shaft,
spilling from the bucket as it comes.

39 Alan Pinnock

He gave me eyes so I could see
the wonders of the world.
Without my eyes I could not see
the other boys and girls.
He gave me ears so I could hear
the wind and rain and sea.
I've got to tell it to the world:
he made me.

He gave me lips so I could speak
and say what's in my mind.
Without my lips I could not speak
a single word or line.
He made my mind so I could think,
and choose what I should be.
I've got to tell it to the world:
he made me.

He gave me hands so I could touch,
and hold a thousand things.
I need my hands to help me write,
to help me fetch and bring.
These feet he made so I could run,
he meant me to be free.
I've got to tell it to the world:
he made me.

40 Traditional

He's got the whole world in his hand.
He's got the whole world in his hand.
He's got the whole world in his hand.
He's got the whole world in his hand.

He's got you and me, brother, in his
    hand. (3)
He's got the whole world in his hand.

He's got you and me, sister, in his
    hand. (3)
He's got the whole world in his hand.

He's got the tiny little baby in his
    hand. (3)
He's got the whole world in his hand.

He's got ev'rybody here in his hand. (3)
He's got the whole world in his hand.

41 Percy Dearmer (1867-1936) after John Bunyan (1628-1688)

He who would valiant be
'gainst all disaster,
let him in constancy
follow the Master.
There's no discouragement
shall make him once relent
his first avowed intent
to be a pilgrim.

Who so beset him round
with dismal stories,
do but themselves confound –
his strength the more is.
No foes shall stay his might,
though he with giants fight:
he will make good his right
to be a pilgrim.

Since, Lord, thou dost defend
us with thy Spirit,
we know we at the end
shall life inherit.
Then fancies flee away!
I'll fear not what men say,
I'll labour night and day
to be a pilgrim.

© Oxford University Press

42 Carl Tuttle, based on Matthew 21:9

Hosanna, hosanna,
hosanna in the highest!
Hosanna, hosanna,
hosanna in the highest!
Lord, we lift up your name
with hearts full of praise;
be exalted, O Lord my God!
Hosanna in the highest!

Glory, glory,
glory to the King of kings!
Glory, glory,
glory to the King of kings!
Lord, we lift up your name
with hearts full of praise;
be exalted, O Lord my God!
Glory to the King of kings!

© 1985 Mercy/Vineyard Publishing/CopyCare Ltd

43 Hugh Mitchell

How did Moses cross the Red Sea?
How did Moses cross the Red Sea?
How did Moses cross the Red Sea?
How did he get across?
Did he swim? No! No!
Did he row? No! No!
Did he jump? No! No! No! No!
Did he drive? No! No!
Did he fly? No! No!
How did he get across?
God blew with his wind, puff, puff,
    puff, puff,
he blew just enough, 'nough, 'nough,
    'nough, 'nough,
and through the sea he made a path,
that's how he got across.

© Zondervan Music Inc., USA/Bucks Music Ltd

44 Unknown

How great is our God,
how great is his name!
How great is our God,
for ever the same!

He rolled back the waters
of the mighty Red Sea,
and he said, 'I'll never leave you.
Put your trust in me.'

He sent his Son, Jesus,
to set us all free,
and he said, 'I'll never leave you.
Put your trust in me.'

He gave us his Spirit,
and now we can see.
And he said, 'I'll never leave you.
Put your trust in me.'

45 v. 1 Leonard E. Smith Jnr, based on Isaiah 52:7-10. vv. 2-4 unknown

How lovely on the mountains are the
    feet of him
who brings good news, good news,
announcing peace, proclaiming news
    of happiness:
our God reigns, our God reigns.

Our God reigns, our God reigns,
our God reigns, our God reigns.

You watchmen, lift your voices
    joyfully as one,
shout for your King, your King!
See eye to eye, the Lord restoring Zion:
our God reigns, our God reigns.

Wasteplaces of Jerusalem,
    break forth with joy!
We are redeemed, redeemed.
The Lord has saved and comforted his
    people:
our God reigns, our God reigns.

Ends of the earth,
    see the salvation of our God!
Jesus is Lord, is Lord!
Before the nations he has bared his
    holy arm:
our God reigns, our God reigns.

© 1974 Thankyou Music

46 Sydney Carter

I danced in the morning when the
   world was begun,
and I danced in the moon and the
   stars and the sun,
and I came down from heaven and I
   danced on the earth,
at Bethlehem I had my birth.

Dance, then, wherever you may be,
I am the Lord of the Dance, said he,
and I'll lead you all, wherever you
   may be,
and I'll lead you all in the dance,
   said he.

I danced for the scribe and the pharisee,
but they would not dance and they
   wouldn't follow me.
I danced for the fishermen, for James
   and John –
they came with me and the dance
   went on.

I danced on the Sabbath and I cured
   the lame;
the holy people said it was a shame.
They whipped and they stripped and
   they hung me on high,
and they left me there on a cross to die.

I danced on a Friday when the sky
   turned black –
it's hard to dance with the devil on
   your back.
They buried my body, and they
   thought I'd gone,
but I am the dance, and I still go on.

They cut me down and I leapt up high;
I am the life that'll never, never die;
I'll live in you if you'll live in me –
I am the Lord of the Dance, said he.

47 Brian Howard

If I were a butterfly,
I'd thank you, Lord, for giving me wings,
and if I were a robin in a tree,
I'd thank you, Lord, that I could sing,
and if I were a fish in the sea,
I'd wiggle my tail and I'd giggle with glee,
but I just thank you, Father, for making
   me 'me'.

For you gave me a heart, and you
   gave me a smile,
you gave me Jesus and you made
   me your child,
and I just thank you, Father, for
   making me 'me'.

If I were an elephant,
I'd thank you, Lord, by raising my trunk,
and if I were a kangaroo,
you know I'd hop right up to you,
and if I were an octopus,
I'd thank you, Lord, for my fine looks,
but I just thank you, Father, for making
   me 'me'.

If I were a wiggly worm,
I'd thank you, Lord, that I could squirm,
and if I were a billy goat,
I'd thank you, Lord, for my strong throat,
and if I were a fuzzy wuzzy bear,
I'd thank you, Lord, for my fuzzy
   wuzzy hair,
but I just thank you, Father, for making
   me 'me'.

48 Estelle White

I give my hands to do your work
and, Jesus Lord, I give them willingly.
I give my feet to go your way
and ev'ry step I shall take cheerfully.

O, the joy of the Lord is my strength,
  my strength!
O, the joy of the Lord is my help,
  my help!
For the pow'r of his Spirit is in my soul
and the joy of the Lord is my strength.

I give my eyes to see the world
and ev'ryone, in just the way you do.
I give my tongue to speak your words,
to spread your name and freedom-
  giving truth.

I give my mind in ev'ry way
so that each thought I have will come
  from you.
I give my spirit to you, Lord,
and every day my prayer will spring
  anew.

I give my heart that you may love
in me your Father and the human race.
I give myself that you may grow
in me and make my life a song of praise.

© 1978 Kevin Mayhew Ltd

49 Susan Sayers

I have a friend who is deeper than the
  ocean,
I have a friend who is wider than the sky,
I have a friend who always
  understands me,
whether I'm happy or ready to cry.

If I am lost he will search until he
  finds me,
if I am scared he will help me to be
  brave.
All I've to do is turn to him and ask him.
I know he'll honour the promise he gave.

'Don't be afraid,' Jesus said, 'for I am
  with you.
Don't be afraid,' Jesus said, 'for I am
  here.
Now and for ever, anywhere you travel,
I shall be with you, I'll always be near.'

© Kevin Mayhew Ltd

50 Charlie Chester and Benny Litchfield

I have seen the golden sunshine,
I have watched the flowers grow,
I have listened to the song birds
and there's one thing now I know,
they were all put there for us to share
by someone so divine,
and if you're a friend of Jesus,
(CLAP CLAP CLAP CLAP)
you're a friend of mine.

I've seen the light, I've seen the light,
and that's why my heart sings.
I've known the joy, I've known the joy
that loving Jesus brings.

I have seen the morning sunshine,
I have heard the oceans roar,
I have seen the flowers of springtime,
and there's one thing I am sure,
they were all put there for us to share
by someone so divine,
and if you're a friend of Jesus,
(CLAP CLAP CLAP CLAP)
you're a friend of mine.

© 1970 by High-Fye Music Ltd

51 Gwen F. Smith

I love the sun,
it shines on me,
God made the sun,
and God made me.

I love the stars,
they twinkle on me,
God made the stars,
and God made me.

I love the rain,
it splashes on me,
God made the rain,
and God made me.

I love the wind,
it blows round me,
God made the wind,
and God made me.

I love the birds,
they sing to me,
God made the birds,
and God made me.

52 Rob Hayward

I'm accepted, I'm forgiven,
I am fathered by the true and living God.
I'm accepted, no condemnation,
I am loved by the true and living God.
There's no guilt or fear as I draw near
to the Saviour and creator of the world.
There is joy and peace as I release
my worship to you, O Lord.

53 Ronald Green, based on words from 1 Corinthians 13

I may speak in the tongues of angels
and foretell with a heavenly song;
should it be that my love is lacking –
then my voice is a sounding gong;

Three things last for ever,
they are faith, hope and love;
and the greatest of these is love,
and the greatest of these is love!

I may give all I have to neighbours,
and explore every mansion above
to possess all the jewels of wisdom –
I am nothing at all, without love;

By my faith I may move the mountains,
and may stand for a cause to be won;
If I do not have love in doing –
then I shall be the better by none;

Now this loving is kind and generous,
and a wonderful, glorious sign
of the limitless, deep, compassion
from the Power, supremely divine;

54 Michael Forster

I'm black, I'm white, I'm short, I'm tall,
I'm all the human race.
I'm young, I'm old, I'm large, I'm small,
and Jesus knows my face.

The love of God is free to ev'ryone
free to ev'ryone, free to ev'ryone.
The love of God is free, oh yes!
That's what the gospel says.

I'm rich, I'm poor, I'm pleased, I'm sad,
I'm ev'ryone you see.
I'm quick, I'm slow, I'm good, I'm bad,
I know that God loves me.

So tall and thin, and short and wide,
and any shade of face,
I'm one of those for whom Christ died,
part of the human race.

56 Graham Kendrick

I'm special because God has loved me,
for he gave the best thing that he had
    to save me;
his own Son, Jesus, crucified to take
    the blame,
for all the bad things I have done.
Thank you, Jesus, thank you, Lord,
for loving me so much.
I know I don't deserve anything;
help me feel your love right now
to know deep in my heart
that I'm your special friend.

55 Geoffrey Gardner

I'm going to paint a perfect picture,
a world of make believe;
no more hunger, war or suffering,
the world I'd like to see.

The blackbird sings in the hedgerow,
the white owl sleeps in the barn,
the brown geese fly, a group in the sky,
the yellow chick pecks the corn.

The stream runs clear through the
    meadow,
the wheat ears swell with the grain,
the oak trees give them shelter and
    shade,
the sunlight bursts through the rain.

The farmers gather the harvest,
the children play by the mill,
the cattle chew and flick up their tails,
the ponies graze on the hill.

57 Hazel Charlton

In the morning early
I go down to the sea
and see the mist on the shore;
I listen, and I listen.

When I go to the rocks
I go looking for shells
and feel the sand beneath my feet;
I listen, and I listen.

When the stormy day comes
waves crash on the cliffs
and the wind whistles through my hair;
I listen, and I listen.

And at night when I sleep
and the sea is calm
the gentle waves lap the shore;
I listen, and I listen.

Continued overleaf

I sometimes think that God
is talking to me
when I hear the sound of the sea;
I listen, and I listen.
I listen, and I listen.

© Hazel Charlton

58 Arthur Scholey

I planted a seed
and now that seed is growing,
oh, how that seed is growing
out of all the ground of me!
I planted a seed,
but there's no way of knowing,
but there's no way of knowing,
is it fruit or flower or weed?
There is no way of showing
'till it blooms for all to see.

I planted a thought
and now that thought is taking,
oh, how that thought is taking
over all the mind of me!
I planted a thought,
and, love or hate, it's breaking,
and, love or hate, it's breaking
out and never will be caught;
and love or hate it's making
of the way you think of me.

I planted a word
and now that word is yelling,
oh, how that word is yelling
out of all the mouth of me!
I planted a word
and truth or lie it's telling,
and truth or lie it's telling
just whenever it is heard.
Whatever it is spelling,
it will soon be clear to see.

I planted a deed
and now that deed is spreading,
oh, how that deed is spreading
far beyond the reach of me!
I planted a deed,
for good or bad it's heading,
for good or bad it's heading –
oh who knows where it will lead?
Should I be glad, or dreading –
here it comes straight back to me!

© Arthur Scholey/Lindsay Music

59 Dan Schutte, based on Isaiah 6

I, the Lord of sea and sky,
I have heard my people cry.
All who dwell in dark and sin
my hand will save.
I, who made the stars of night,
I will make their darkness bright.
Who will bear my light to them?
Whom shall I send?

Here am I, Lord. Is it I, Lord?
I have heard you calling in the night.
I will go, Lord, if you lead me.
I will hold your people in my heart.

I, the Lord of snow and rain,
I have borne my people's pain.
I have wept for love of them.
They turn away.
I will break their hearts of stone,
give them hearts for love alone.
I will speak my word to them.
Whom shall I send?

I, the Lord of wind and flame,
I will tend the poor and lame.
I will set a feast for them.
My hand will save.
Finest bread I will provide
till their hearts are satisfied.
I will give my life to them.
Whom shall I send?

60 Geoffrey Gardner

It's a new day, there's hope,
it's a new day, there's scope,
to face a different challenge,
discover there's no end
to new beginnings
to the new things we can do.

It's a new task, there's hope,
it's a new task, there's scope,
to face a different challenge,
discover there's no end
to new beginnings,
to the new things we can do.

It's a new skill, there's hope,
it's a new skill, there's scope . . .

It's a new friend, there's hope,
it's a new friend, there's scope . . .

61 John Glynn

I watch the sunrise lighting the sky,
casting its shadows near.
And on this morning, bright though
   it be,
I feel those shadows near me.

But you are always close to me,
following all my ways.
May I be always close to you,
following all your ways, Lord.

I watch the sunlight shine through the
   clouds,
warming the earth below.
And at midday, life seems to say:
'I feel your brightness near me.'

For you are always . . .

I watch the sunset fading away,
lighting the clouds with sleep.
And as the evening closes its eyes,
I feel your presence near me.

For you are always . . .

I watch the moonlight guarding the
   night,
waiting till morning comes.
The air is silent, earth is at rest
— only your peace is near me.

Yes, you are always . . .

62 Tom McGuinness

I will bring to you the best gift I can
   offer;
I will sing to you the best things in
   my mind.

Paper pictures, bits of string, I'll bring
   you almost anything,
I'll bring a song that only I can sing:
the rainbow colours in the sky, the
   misty moon that caught my eye,
the magic of a new-born butterfly.

Continued overleaf

I'll bring a song of winter trees, the
  skidding ice, the frozen leaves,
the battles in our snowball-shouting
  streets.
I'll bring you summers I have known,
  adventure trips and journeys home,
the summer evenings playing down
  our road.

I will bring to you the best gift I can
  offer;
I will sing to you the best things in
  my mind.

I'll share my secrets and my dreams,
  I'll show you wonders I have seen,
and I will listen when you speak your
  name;
and if you really want me to, I will
  share my friends with you,
everyone at home and in my school.

© Tom McGuinness

63 Max Dyer

I will sing, I will sing a song unto the
  Lord. (3)
Alleluia, glory to the Lord.

We will come, we will come as one
  before the Lord. (3)
Alleluia, glory to the Lord.

If the Son, if the Son shall make you
  free, (3)
you shall be free indeed.

They that sow in tears shall reap in
  joy. (3)
Alleluia, glory to the Lord.

Ev'ry knee shall bow and ev'ry tongue
  confess (3)
that Jesus Christ is Lord.

In his name, in his name we have the
  victory. (3)
Alleluia, glory to the Lord.

© 1974 Celebration/Thankyou Music

64 Margaret Cropper, adapt. Stephen Hopkinson

Jesus' hands were kind hands,
  doing good to all,
healing pain and sickness,
  blessing children small,
and my hands should serve him,
  ready at his call.
Jesus' hands were kind hands,
  doing good to all.

© Stainer & Bell Ltd

65 H. W. Rattle

Jesus' love is very wonderful,
Jesus' love is very wonderful,
Jesus' love is very wonderful,
oh wonderful love!
So high you can't get over it,
so low you can't get under it,
so wide you can't get round it,
oh wonderful love!

© Scripture Union

66 Graham Kendrick

Jesus put this song into our hearts,
Jesus put this song into our hearts;
it's a song of joy no one can take away.
Jesus put this song into our hearts.

Jesus taught us how to live in harmony,
Jesus taught us how to live in harmony;
diff'rent faces, diff'rent races, he made
    us one.
Jesus taught us how to live in harmony.

Jesus turned our sorrow into dancing,
Jesus turned our sorrow into dancing;
changed our tears of sadness into
    rivers of joy.
Jesus turned our sorrow into a dance.

Each verse should be sung faster.

© 1986 Thankyou Music

67 Fred Dunn

Jubilate, ev'rybody,
serve the Lord in all your ways,
and come before his presence singing,
enter now his courts with praise.
For the Lord our God is gracious,
and his mercy everlasting.
Jubilate, jubilate, jubilate Deo!

© 1977 Thankyou Music

68 Spiritual

Kum ba yah, my Lord, kum ba yah,
kum ba yah, my Lord, kum ba yah,
kum ba yah, my Lord, kum ba yah,
O Lord, kum ba yah.

Someone's crying, Lord, kum ba yah . . .

Someone's singing, Lord, kum ba yah . . .

Someone's praying, Lord, kum ba yah . . .

69 Sy Miller and Jill Jackson

Let there be peace on earth
and let it begin with me;
let there be peace on earth,
the peace that was meant to be,
with God as our Father,
brothers all are we
let me walk with my brother
in perfect harmony.

Let peace begin with me,
let this be the moment now.
With ev'ry step I take,
let this be my solemn vow:
to take each moment and live
each moment in peace eternally.
Let there be peace on earth
and let it begin with me.

© 1956 Jan-Lee Music/Universal/Music Sales

70 Michael Forster

Life for the poor was hard and tough,
Jesus said, 'That's not good enough;
life should be great and here's the sign:
I'll turn the water into wine.'

*Jesus turned the water into wine, (3)
and the people saw that life was
good.*

Life is a thing to be enjoyed,
not to be wasted or destroyed.
Laughter is part of God's design;
let's turn the water into wine!

Go to the lonely and the sad,
give them the news to make them glad,
helping the light of hope to shine,
turning the water into wine!

© Kevin Mayhew Ltd

71 Peggy Blakeley

Look for signs that summer's done,
winter's drawing near.
Watch the changing colours come,
turning of the year.
See the flowers' final blaze
in the morning's misty haze,
sing a thankful song of praise,
autumn time is here.

See the fields are bare and brown,
feel the nights turn cold.
Lamps are early lit in town,
hunter's moon shines gold.
Thank you, God, for rest and food,
for the harvest safely stored,
sing a song to praise the Lord
as the year grows old.

© A & C Black Publishers Ltd

72 Patrick Appleford

Lord Jesus Christ, you have come to us,
you are one with us, Mary's Son;
cleansing our souls from all their sin,
pouring your love and goodness in,
Jesus, our love for you we sing,
living Lord.

Lord Jesus Christ, now and ev'ry day
teach us how to pray, Son of God.
You have commanded us to do
this in remembrance, Lord, of you,
into our lives your pow'r breaks through,
living Lord.

Lord Jesus Christ, you have come to us,
born as one of us, Mary's Son.
Led out to die on Calvary,
risen from death to set us free,
living Lord Jesus, help us see
you are Lord.

Lord Jesus Christ, I would come to you,
live my life for you, Son of God.
All your commands I know are true,
your many gifts will make me new,
into my life your pow'r breaks through,
living Lord.

© 1960 Josef Weinberger Ltd

73 Jan Struther

Lord of all hopefulness, Lord of all joy,
whose trust, ever childlike, no cares
    could destroy,
be there at our waking and give us,
    we pray,
your bliss in our hearts, Lord, at the
    break of the day.

Lord of all eagerness, Lord of all faith,
whose strong hands were skilled at
the plane and the lathe,
be there at our labours and give us,
we pray,
your strength in our hearts, Lord, at
the noon of the day.

Lord of all kindliness, Lord of all grace,
your hands swift to welcome, your
arms to embrace,
be there at our homing and give us,
we pray,
your love in our hearts, Lord, at the
eve of the day.

Lord of all gentleness, Lord of all calm,
whose voice is contentment, whose
presence is balm,
be there at our sleeping and give us,
we pray,
your peace in our hearts, Lord, at the
end of the day.

© Oxford University Press

74 Jancis Harvey

*Lord of the harvest, Lord of the field,
give thanks now to God in nature
revealed.*

Give thanks for the sun, the wind and
the rain
and thanks for the crops that feed us
again.
The corn safely cut is gathered inside
we thank you, oh Lord, that you can
provide.

The trees ripe with fruit stand proud
in the sun,
we gather them now that summer is
gone.
For yours is the wonder, yours is the
power,
yours is the glory of fruit and of flower.

So in all our plenty, help us to see,
the needs all around whatever they be.
With food for the body, strength for
the soul,
it's healing and caring, making them
whole.

© Jancis Harvey

75 Graham Kendrick

Lord, the light of your love is shining,
in the midst of the darkness, shining,
Jesus, Light of the World, shine upon us,
set us free by the truth you now bring
us,
shine on me, shine on me.

*Shine, Jesus, shine,
fill this land with the Father's glory,
blaze, Spirit, blaze, set our hearts
on fire.
Flow, river, flow,
flood the nations with grace and
mercy;
send forth your word, Lord,
and let there be light!*

Lord, I come to your awesome presence,
from the shadows into your radiance;
by the blood I may enter your brightness,
search me, try me, consume all my
darkness.
Shine on me, shine on me.

Continued overleaf

As we gaze on your kingly brightness,
so our faces display your likeness,
ever changing from glory to glory,
mirrored here, may our lives tell your
    story.
Shine on me, shine on me.

Shine, Jesus, shine,
fill this land with the Father's glory,
blaze, Spirit, blaze, set our hearts
    on fire.
Flow, river, flow,
flood the nations with grace and
    mercy;
send forth your word, Lord,
and let there be light!

76 Malvina Reynolds

Love is something if you give it away,
give it away, give it away,
love is something if you give it away,
you end up having more.

It's just like a magic penny;
Hold it tight and you won't have any;
Lend it, spend it, and you'll have so
    many,
they'll roll all over the floor, for . . .

So let's go dancing till the break of day,
and if there's a piper, we can pay.
For love is something if you give it
    away,
you end up having more.

77 Patrick Appleford, based on words from 1 Corinthians 13

Love will never come to an end,
love will never come to an end,
three things will last:
faith, hope and love,
but greatest of all is love,
love, love, love.

Like an angel I may speak,
know the truths that others seek,
give my goods and life away,
I am nothing without love.

I may seem a great success,
wisdom, wealth or charm possess,
yet whatever I achieve
I am nothing without love.

Love is patient, love is kind.
Love requires a truthful mind.
Love will keep no score of wrongs.
There is nothing love can't face.

Childish thoughts are put away,
partial knowledge has its day.
Love with faith and hope endures,
there is nothing conquers love.

Love will never come to an end,
love will never come to an end,
three things will last:
faith, hope and love,
but greatest of all is love,
love, love, love.
Love is forever,
for ever and ever, is love.

78 Sebastian Temple, based on the Prayer of St Francis of Assisi

Make me a channel of your peace.
Where there is hatred, let me bring
    your love.
Where there is injury, your pardon, Lord,
and where there's doubt, true faith in
    you.

Make me a channel of your peace.
Where there's despair in life, let me
    bring hope.
Where there is darkness, only light,
and where there's sadness, ever joy.

O Master, grant that I may never seek
so much to be consoled as to console,
to be understood, as to understand,
to be loved, as to love with all my soul.

Make me a channel of your peace.
It is in pardoning that we are pardoned,
in giving of ourselves that we receive,
and in dying that we're born to eternal
    life.

© 1967 OCP Publications

79 Peggy Blakeley

Milk bottle tops and paper bags,
iron bedsteads, dirty old rags,
litter on the pavement,
paper in the park,
is this what we
    (CLAP CLAP CLAP CLAP)
really want to see?
    (CLAP CLAP CLAP-CLAP CLAP)
No! No! No!

Old plastic bottles, silver foil,
chocolate wrapping, engine oil,
rubbish in the gutter,
junk upon the beach,
is this what we
    (CLAP CLAP CLAP CLAP)
really want to see?
    (CLAP CLAP CLAP-CLAP CLAP)
No! No! No!

Help us, Lord, to find each day
ways to help to keep away
that litter off the pavement,
that rubbish off the beach.
For this is what we
    (CLAP CLAP CLAP CLAP)
really want to see.
    (CLAP CLAP CLAP-CLAP CLAP)
Yes! Yes! Yes!

© A & C Black Publishers Ltd

80 Trish Mondoza

Mister Noah built an ark,
the people thought it such a lark.
Mister Noah pleaded so,
but into the ark they would not go.

Down came the rain in torrents,
    (splish, splash)
down came the rain in torrents,
    (splish, splash)
down came the rain in torrents
and only eight were saved.

The animals went in two by two,
elephant, giraffe and kangaroo.
All were safely stowed away,
on that great and awful day.

Continued overleaf

Whenever you see a rainbow,
whenever you see a rainbow,
whenever you see a rainbow,
remember that God is love.

81 Eleanor Farjeon

Morning has broken like the first
    morning,
blackbird has spoken like the first bird.
Praise for the singing! Praise for the
    morning!
Praise for them, springing fresh from
    the Word!

Sweet the rain's new fall, sunlit from
    heaven,
like the first dew-fall on the first grass.
Praise for the sweetness of the wet
    garden,
sprung in completeness where his feet
    pass.

Mine is the sunlight! Mine is the
    morning,
born of the one light Eden saw play.
Praise with elation, praise ev'ry morning,
God's re-creation of the new day!

82 Traditional

My God is so big, so strong and
*   so mighty,*
there's nothing that he cannot do.
My God is so big, so strong and
*   so mighty,*
there's nothing that he cannot do.

The rivers are his, the mountains are his,
the stars are his handiwork too.
My God is so big, so strong and
    so mighty,
there's nothing that he cannot do.

He's called you to live for him ev'ry day,
in all that you say and you do.
My God is so big, so strong and
    so mighty,
there's nothing that he cannot do.

83 Patrick Appleford

O Lord, all the world belongs to you,
and you are always making all things
    new.
What is wrong you forgive,
and the new life you give
is what's turning the world upside
    down.

The world's only loving to its friends,
but you have brought us love that
    never ends;
loving enemies too,
and this loving with you
is what's turning the world upside
    down.

This world lives divided and apart.
You draw us all together and we start,
in your body, to see
that in fellowship we
can be turning the world upside down.

The world wants the wealth to live in
    state,
but you show us a new way to be great:
like a servant you came,
and if we do the same,
we'll be turning the world upside down.

O Lord, all the world belongs to you,
and you are always making all things
    new.
Send your Spirit on all
in your church, whom you call
to be turning the world upside down.

84 Karl Boberg, trans. Stuart K. Hine

O Lord, my God, when I, in awesome
    wonder,
consider all the works thy hand has
    made,
I see the stars, I hear the rolling thunder,
thy pow'r throughout the universe
    displayed.

Then sings my soul, my Saviour
    God, to thee:
how great thou art, how great
    thou art.
Then sings my soul, my Saviour God,
    to thee:
how great thou art, how great
    thou art.

When through the woods and forest
    glades I wander,
and hear the birds sing sweetly in the
    trees;
when I look down from lofty mountain
    grandeur,
and hear the brook, and feel the gentle
    breeze.

And when I think that God, his Son
    not sparing,
sent him to die, I scarce can take it in
that on the cross, my burden gladly
    bearing,
he bled and died to take away my sin.

When Christ shall come with shout of
    acclamation,
and take me home, what joy shall fill
    my heart;
when I shall bow in humble adoration,
and there proclaim: my God, how
    great thou art.

85 Michael Forster

One hundred and fifty-three!
One hundred and fifty-three!
The number of all the fish in the sea:
one hundred and fifty-three!

We'd fished all the night for nothing,
but Jesus said, 'Try once more.'
So we doubtfully tried
on the other side
and found there were fish galore!

We got all the fish to the shore,
we wondered how many there'd be.
So we started to count,
and what an amount:
one hundred and fifty-three!

Now here was a wonderful sight
we'd never expected to see;
and the net didn't break,
it was able to take
the hundred and fifty-three!

So whether you're rich or you're poor,
whatever your race or your sect,
be you black, white or brown,
Jesus wants you around,
there's plenty of room in the net!

86 Sydney Carter

One more step along the world I go,
one more step along the world I go.
From the old things to the new
keep me travelling along with you.

*And it's from the old I travel to the
new,
keep me travelling along with you.*

Round the corners of the world I turn,
more and more about the world I learn.
All the new things that I see
you'll be looking at along with me.

As I travel through the bad and good,
keep me travelling the way I should.
Where I see no way to go
you'll be telling me the way, I know.

Give me courage when the world is
rough,
keep me loving though the world is
tough.
Leap and sing in all I do,
keep me travelling along with you.

You are older than the world can be,
you are younger than the life in me.
Ever old and ever new,
keep me travelling along with you.

87 Matthew 6:9-13; Luke 11:2-4

Our Father, who art in heaven,
hallowèd be thy name.
Thy kingdom come, thy will be done,
*hallowèd be thy name,
hallowèd be thy name.*

On earth as it is in heaven.
Give us this day our daily bread.

Forgive us our trespasses,
as we forgive those who trespass
against us.

Lead us not into temptation,
but deliver us from all that is evil.

For thine is the kingdom, the pow'r
and the glory,
for ever and for ever and ever.

Amen, amen, it shall be so,
amen, amen, it shall be so.

88 Estelle White

O what a wonderful world!
O what a wonderful world it is!
O what a wonderful world!
Thank you, heav'nly Father.

O what a beautiful world!
O what a beautiful world it is!
O what a beautiful world!
Thank you, my Lord Jesus.

O what a marvellous world!
O what a marvellous world it is!
O what a marvellous world!
Thank you, Holy Spirit.

89 Traditional

O when the saints go marching in,
O when the saints go marching in,
I want to be in that number
when the saints go marching in.

O when they crown him Lord of all . . .

O when all knees bow at his name . . .

O when they sing the Saviour's
praise . . .

O when the saints go marching in . . .

Love, perfect love . . .

Faith, perfect faith . . .

Hope, perfect hope . . .

Joy, perfect joy . . .

90 Unknown

Peace is flowing like a river,
flowing out through you and me,
spreading out into the desert,
setting all the captives free.

*Let it flow through me,
let it flow through me,
let the mighty peace of God
flow out through me.
(Repeat)*

Love is flowing like a river . . .

Joy is flowing like a river . . .

Faith is flowing like a river . . .

Hope is flowing like a river . . .

91 Kevin Mayhew

Peace, perfect peace,
is the gift of Christ our Lord.
Peace, perfect peace,
is the gift of Christ our Lord.
Thus, says the Lord,
will the world know my friends.
Peace, perfect peace,
is the gift of Christ our Lord.

92 Paul Booth

Pears and apples, wheat and grapes,
many textures, many shapes;
falling leaves in golden drifts
thank you, God, for harvest gifts.

Flashing shoals of silver fish,
every colour you could wish;
fishing boats, for you and me
reap the harvest of the sea.

Deep beneath the ocean floor
fuel and power have lain in store,
brought to us through dangerous toil
thank you, God, for gas and oil.

Coal black diamonds in the earth,
ancient forests gave them birth;
skill and labour now combine
reaping harvests of the mine.

Earth and ocean, plant and beast,
altogether make the feast;
all who long to share your grace
at your table have their place.

Loving Lord, we know you care;
may we all your goodness share;
save us from all selfish greed,
finding you in those in need.

93 John Kennett

Praise him on the trumpet,
the psaltery and harp,
praise him on the timbrel and the dance;
praise him with stringed instruments
   too.
Praise him on the loud cymbals,
praise him on the loud cymbals,
let ev'rything that has breath
praise the Lord.

Hallelujah, praise the Lord,
hallelujah, praise the Lord,
let ev'rything that has breath
praise the Lord.
(Repeat)

94 Peter Casey

Praise the Lord in the rhythm of your
   music,
praise the Lord in the freedom of your
   dance,
praise the Lord in the country and the
   city,
praise him in the living of your life!

Praise the Lord on the organ and piano,
praise the Lord on guitar and on the
   drums,
praise the Lord on the tambourine
   and cymbals,
praise him in the singing of your song!

Praise the Lord with the movement of
   your bodies,
praise the Lord with the clapping of
   your hands,
praise the Lord with your poetry and
   painting,
praise him in the acting of your play!

Praise the Lord in the feeding of the
   hungry,
praise the Lord in the healing of
   disease,
praise the Lord as you show his love
   in action,
praise him in your caring for the poor!

Praise the Lord, every nation, every
   people,
praise the Lord, men and women, old
   and young,
praise the Lord, let us celebrate together,
praise him everything in heaven and
   earth!

95 Evelyn Tarner, based on Philippians 4:4

Rejoice in the Lord always,
and again I say rejoice.
(Repeat)
Rejoice, rejoice,
and again I say rejoice.
(Repeat)

This song may be sung as a round.

96 Peter Ratcliffe

Riding out across the desert,
travelling over sandy plains,
comes a company of wise men,
moving steadily along their way;
leaving all their friends behind them,
guided by the star so bright,
now they've got to keep on going
must not let the star get out of sight.

Riding through the desert,
gently the wise men go,
onwards to the king,
who was promised long ago;
but they don't know where they're
going to find him,
there's many towns to search,
so they'll keep on following the star,
for it will lead them to his place of
birth.

Wise men on their desert journey,
travelled many miles so far,
though they're getting tired and weary,
town of Bethlehem is not too far:
how they long to worship Jesus
and honour him with royal gifts,
hearts are full of joy and wonder,
as they're searching for the new born
king.

© Copyright Peter Ratcliffe/Jubilate Hymns

97 Unknown, based on Genesis 6:4

Rise and shine, and give God his
glory, glory, (3)
children of the Lord.

The Lord said to Noah, 'There's gonna
be a floody, floody.'
Lord said to Noah, 'There's gonna be
a floody, floody.
Get those children out of the muddy,
muddy,
children of the Lord.'

So Noah, he built him, he built him an
arky, arky,
Noah, he built him, he built him an
arky, arky,
built it out of hickory barky, barky,
children of the Lord.

The animals, they came on, they came
on, by twosies, twosies,
animals, they came on, they came on,
by twosies, twosies,
elephants and kangaroosies, roosies,
children of the Lord.

It rained and poured for forty daysies,
daysies,
rained and poured for forty daysies,
daysies,
nearly drove those animals crazies,
crazies,
children of the Lord.

The sun came out and dried up the
landy, landy,
sun came out and dried up the landy,
landy,
ev'rything was fine and dandy, dandy,
children of the Lord.

Continued overleaf

If you get to heaven before I do-sies,
   do-sies,
you get to heaven before I do-sies,
   do-sies,
tell those angels I'm comin' too-sies,
   too-sies,
children of the Lord.

98 Sydney Carter

Said Judas to Mary, 'Now what will
   you do
with your ointment so rich and so rare?'
'I'll pour it all over the feet of the Lord,
and I'll wipe it away with my hair,' she
   said,
'I'll wipe it away with my hair.'

'Oh Mary, oh Mary, oh think of the poor,
this ointment, it could have been sold,
and think of the blankets and think of
   the bread
you could buy with the silver and gold,'
   he said,
'you could buy with the silver and gold.'

'Tomorrow, tomorrow, I'll think of the
   poor,
tomorrow,' she said, 'not today;
for dearer than all of the poor in the
   world
is my love who is going away,' she said,
'is my love who is going away.'

Said Jesus to Mary, 'Your love is so deep,
today you may do as you will.
Tomorrow you say I am going away,
but my body I leave with you still,' he
   said,
'my body I leave with you still.'

'The poor of the world are my body,'
   he said,
'to the end of the world they shall be.
The bread and the blankets you give
   to the poor
you'll know you have given to me,' he
   said,
'you'll know you have given to me.'

'My body will hang on the cross of
   the world,
tomorrow,' he said, 'and today,
and Martha and Mary will find me again
and wash all the sorrow away,' he said,
'and wash all the sorrow away.'

© 1964 Stainer & Bell Ltd

99 v. 1: Karen Lafferty; vv. 2 & 3: unknown, based on Matthew 6:33; 7:7

Seek ye first the kingdom of God,
and his righteousness,
and all these things shall be added
   unto you;
allelu, alleluia.

   Alleluia, alleluia,
   alleluia,
   allelu, alleluia.

You shall not live by bread alone,
but by ev'ry word
that proceeds from the mouth of God;
allelu, alleluia.

Ask and it shall be given unto you,
seek and ye shall find;
knock and it shall be opened unto you;
allelu, alleluia.

© 1972 Maranatha! Music/CopyCare Ltd

100 Sandra Joan Billington

Shalom, my friends,
shalom, my friends,
shalom, shalom.
The peace of Christ I give you today,
shalom, shalom.

101 Traditional, adapted by Geoffrey Gardner

Shalom, shalom,
may peace be with you,
throughout your days;
in all that you do,
may peace be with you,
shalom, shalom.

This song may be sung as a round.

102 Margaret Old, adapted by Geoffrey Marshall-Taylor

Spirit of God, as strong as the wind,
gentle as is the dove,
give us your joy, and give us your
peace,
show to us Jesus' love.

You inspired men, long, long ago,
they then proclaimed your word;
we see their lives, serving mankind:
through them your voice is heard.

Without your help, we fail our Lord,
we cannot live his way,
we need your power, we need your
strength,
following Christ each day.

103 Geoffrey Gardner

Spirit of peace, come to our waiting
world;
throughout the nations, may your voice
be heard.
Unlock the door of hope, for you hold
the key;
Spirit of peace, come to our world.

Spirit of love, come to our waiting world;
throughout the nations, may your voice
be heard.
Unlock the door of hope, for you hold
the key;
Spirit of love, come to our world.

Spirit of strength, come to our waiting
world;
throughout the nations, may your voice
be heard.
Unlock the door of hope, for you hold
the key;
Spirit of strength, come to our world.

Spirit of light, come to our waiting
world;
throughout the nations, may your voice
be heard.
Unlock the door of hope, for you hold
the key;
Spirit of light, come to our world.

Spirit of God, come to our waiting world;
throughout the nations, may your voice
be heard.
Unlock the door of hope, for you hold
the key;
Spirit of God, come to our world.
Spirit of God, come to our world.

104 Peter Lewis

Sunday, Monday, Tuesday, Wednesday;
Thursday, Friday Saturday, too.
One, two, three, four, five, six, seven
    days:
each day diff'rent and ev'ry day new.

Wet days, dry days, bright days,
    cloudy days,
hot days, cold days, windy days, too.
One, two, three, four, five, six, seven
    days:
each day diff'rent and ev'ry day new.

High days, low days, sad days, happy
    days,
good days, bad days, other days, too.
One, two, three, four, five, six, seven
    days:
each day diff'rent and ev'ry day new.

Work days, rest days, wash-days,
    shopping-days,
birthdays, sports-days, holidays, too.
One, two, three, four, five, six, seven
    days:
each day diff'rent and ev'ry day new.

© Peter Lewis

105 Susan Sayers

Thank you for the summer morning,
misting into heat;
thank you for the diamonds
of dew beneath my feet;
thank you for the silver
where a snail has wandered by;
oh, we praise the name
of him who made
the earth and sea and sky.

Thank you for the yellow fields
of corn like waving hair;
thank you for the red surprise
of poppies here and there;
thank you for the blue of
an electric dragonfly;
oh, we praise the name
of him who made
the earth and sea and sky.

Thank you for the splintered light
among the brooding trees;
thank you for the leaves that rustle
in a sudden breeze;
thank you for the branches
and the fun of climbing high;
oh, we praise the name
of him who made
the earth and sea and sky.

Thank you for the evening
as the light begins to fade;
clouds so red and purple
that the setting sun has made;
thank you for the shadows
as the owls come gliding by;
oh, we praise the name
of him who made
the earth and sea and sky.

© Kevin Mayhew Ltd

106 Diane Andrew, adapted by Geoffrey Marshall-Taylor

Thank you, Lord, for this new day, (3)
right where we are.

    Alleluia, praise the Lord, (3)
    right where we are.

Thank you, Lord, for food to eat, (3)
right where we are.

Thank you, Lord, for clothes to wear, (3)
right where we are.

Thank you, Lord, for all your gifts, (3)
right where we are.

107 Sydney Carter

The bell of creation is swinging for ever
in all of the things that are coming to
    be,
the bell of creation is swinging for ever
and all of the while it is swinging in me.

Swing, bell, over the land!
Swing, bell, under the sea!
The bell of creation is swinging for
    ever
and all of the while it is swinging in
    me.

In all of my loving, in all of my labour,
in all of the things that are coming to
    be,
in all of my loving, in all of my labour,
the bell of creation is swinging in me.

I look for the life that is living for ever
in all of the things that are coming to
    be,
I look for the life that is living for ever,
and all of the while it is looking for me.

I'll swing with the bell that is swinging
    for ever,
in all of the things that are coming to
    be,
I'll swing with the bell that is swinging
    for ever,
and all of the while it is swinging in me.

108 David Arkin

The ink is black, the page is white,
together we learn to read and write,
to read and write;
and now a child can understand
this is the law of all the land,
all the land;
the ink is black, the page is white,
together we learn to read and write,
to read and write.

The slate is black, the chalk is white,
the words stand out so clear and bright,
so clear and bright;
and now at last we plainly see
the alphabet of liberty,
liberty;
the slate is black, the chalk is white,
together we learn to read and write,
to read and write.

A child is black, a child is white,
the whole world looks upon the sight,
upon the sight;
for very well the whole world knows
this is the way that freedom grows,
freedom grows;
a child is black, a child is white,
together we learn to read and write,
to read and write.

Continued overleaf

The world is black, the world is white,
it turns by day and then by night,
and then by night;
it turns so each and ev'ry one
can take his station in the sun,
in the sun;
The world is black, the world is white,
together we learn to read and write,
to read and write.

109 John Gowans

There are hundreds of sparrows,
    thousands, millions,
they're two a penny, far too many
    there must be;
there are hundreds and thousands,
    millions of sparrows,
but God knows ev'ry one, and God
    knows me.

There are hundreds of flowers,
    thousands, millions,
and flowers fair the meadows wear for
    all to see;
there are hundreds and thousands,
    millions of flowers,
but God knows ev'ry one, and God
    knows me.

There are hundreds of planets,
    thousands, millions,
way out in space each has a place by
    God's decree;
there are hundreds and thousands,
    millions of planets,
but God knows ev'ry one, and God
    knows me.

There are hundreds of children,
    thousands, millions,
and yet their names are written on
    God's memory;
there are hundreds and thousands,
    millions of children,
but God knows ev'ry one, and God
    knows me.

110 Cecil Frances Alexander, alt.

There is a green hill far away,
outside a city wall,
where Christ our Lord was crucified,
who died to save us all.

We may not know, we cannot tell,
what pains he had to bear,
but we believe it was for us
he hung and suffered there.

He died that we could be forgiv'n,
that God might call us good,
that we might go at last to heav'n,
saved by his precious blood.

O dearly, dearly has he loved,
so let us love him too,
and trust in his redeeming blood,
and try his works to do.

111 Geoffrey Marshall-Taylor

There is singing in the desert,
    there is laughter in the skies,
there are wise men filled with wonder,
    there are shepherds with surprise,
you can tell the world is dancing
    by the light that's in their eyes,
for Jesus Christ is here.

Come and sing aloud your praises,
come and sing aloud your praises,
come and sing aloud your praises,
for Jesus Christ is here.

He hears deaf men by the lakeside,
    he sees blind men in the streets,
he goes up to those who cannot walk,
    he talks to all he meets,
touching silken robes or tattered
    clothes, it's everyone he greets,
for Jesus Christ is here.

There is darkness on the hillside,
    there is sorrow in the town,
there's a man upon a wooden cross,
    a man who's gazing down,
you can see the marks of love
    and not the furrows of a frown,
for Jesus Christ is here.

There is singing in the desert,
    there is laughter in the skies,
there are wise men filled with wonder,
    there are shepherds with surprise,
you can tell the world is dancing
    by the light that's in their eyes,
for Jesus Christ is here.

112 Damian Lundy

The Spirit lives to set us free,
walk, walk in the light.
He binds us all in unity,
walk, walk in the light.

Walk in the light, (3)
walk in the light of the Lord.

Jesus promised life to all,
walk, walk in the light.
The dead were wakened by his call,
walk, walk in the light.

He died in pain on Calvary,
walk, walk in the light,
to save the lost like you and me,
walk, walk in the light.

We know his death was not the end,
walk, walk in the light.
He gave his Spirit to be our friend,
walk, walk in the light.

By Jesus' love our wounds are healed,
walk, walk in the light.
The Father's kindness is revealed,
walk, walk in the light.

The Spirit lives in you and me,
walk, walk in the light.
His light will shine for all to see,
walk, walk in the light.

113 Michael Forster

The world is full of smelly feet,
weary from the dusty street.
The world is full of smelly feet,
we'll wash them for each other.

Jesus said to his disciples,
'Wash those weary toes!
Do it in a cheerful fashion,
never hold your nose!'

People on a dusty journey
need a place to rest;
Jesus says, 'You say you love me,
this will be the test!'

Continued overleaf

We're his friends, we recognise him
in the folk we meet;
smart or scruffy, we'll still love him,
wash his smelly feet.

114 Susan Sayers

Think big: an elephant.
Think bigger: a submarine.
Think bigger: the highest mountain
that anyone has ever seen.
Yet big, big, bigger is God,
and he loves us all!

Think old: a vintage car.
Think older: a full grown tree.
Think older: a million grains
of the sand beside the surging sea.
Yet old, old, older is God,
and he loves us all!

Think strong: a tiger's jaw.
Think stronger: a castle wall.
Think stronger: a hurricane
that leaves little standing there at all.
Yet strong, strong, stronger is God,
and he loves us all!

115 Tom McGuinness (adapted)

Think of all the things we lose,
so many things, I get confused:
our pencil sharpeners, favourite books,
our indoor shoes and outdoor boots,
pocket money down the drain,
then felt-tip pens and people's names.
The worst of all things to be lost
is just a friend you really trust.

Think of all the things we find,
so many things I bring to mind:
in lofts and cupboards, if you browse,
are old tin whistles, acting clothes,
clocks that used to chime, and bits
of engines and of building kits:
but even better, I believe,
is just a friend to share them with.

Think of times we lose our nerves,
we're feeling sad and no one cares:
an empty feeling deep inside,
there's nowhere else for us to hide.
That's the time to call a friend
whom we can never lose again:
there's one friend who is very near,
a friend who takes away our fear.

116 Doreen Newport

Think of a world without any flowers,
think of a world without any trees,
think of a sky without any sunshine,
think of the air without any breeze.
We thank you, Lord, for flow'rs and
    trees and sunshine,
we thank you, Lord, and praise your
    holy name.

Think of a world without any animals,
think of a field without any herd,
think of a stream without any fishes,
think of a dawn without any bird.
We thank you, Lord, for all your living
    creatures,
we thank you, Lord, and praise your
    holy name.

Think of a world without any people,
think of a street with no one living there,
think of a town without any houses,
no one to love and nobody to care.
We thank you, Lord, for families and
    friendships,
we thank you, Lord, and praise your
    holy name.

117 Les Garrett

This is the day, this is the day
that the Lord has made, that the Lord
    has made;
we will rejoice, we will rejoice,
and be glad in it, and be glad in it.
This is the day that the Lord has made;
we will rejoice and be glad in it.
This is the day, this is the day
that the Lord has made.

This is the day, this is the day
when he rose again, when he rose again;
we will rejoice, we will rejoice,
and be glad in it, and be glad in it.
This is the day when he rose again;
we will rejoice and be glad in it.
This is the day, this is the day
when he rose again.

This is the day, this is the day
when the Spirit came, when the Spirit
    came;
we will rejoice, we will rejoice,
and be glad in it, and be glad in it.
This is the day when the Spirit came;
we will rejoice and be glad in it.
This is the day, this is the day
when the Spirit came.

118 Traditional, alt.

*This little light of mine, I'm gonna
    let it shine, (3)
let it shine, let it shine, let it shine.*

The light that shines is the light of love,
lights the darkness from above,
it shines on me and it shines on you,
and shows what the power of love
    can do.
I'm gonna shine my light both far and
    near,
I'm gonna shine my light both bright
    and clear.
Where there's a dark corner in this land,
I'm gonna let my little light shine.

On Monday he gave me the gift of love.
Tuesday peace came from above.
On Wednesday he told me to have
    more faith.
On Thursday he gave me a little more
    grace.
Friday he told me just to watch and
    pray.
Saturday he told me just what to say.
On Sunday he gave me the pow'r divine
to let my little light shine.

119 Sydney Carter

Travel on, travel on, there's a river that
    is flowing,
a river that is flowing night and day.
Travel on, travel on to the river that is
    flowing,
the river will be with you all the way.
Travel on, travel on to the river that is
    flowing,
the river will be with you all the way.

Continued overleaf

Travel on, travel on, there's a flower
that is growing,
a flower that is growing night and day.
Travel on, travel on to the flower that
is growing,
the flower will be with you all the way.
Travel on, travel on to the flower that
is growing,
the flower will be with you all the way.

Travel on, travel on to the music that
is playing,
the music that is playing night and day.
Travel on, travel on to the music that
is playing,
the music will be with you all the way.
Travel on, travel on to the music that
is playing,
the music will be with you all the way.

In the kingdom of heaven is my end
and my beginning
and the road that I must follow night
and day.
Travel on, travel on to the kingdom
that is coming,
the kingdom will be with you all the
way.
Travel on, travel on to the kingdom
that is coming,
the kingdom will be with you all the
way.

120 Traditional (adapted Geoffrey Marshall-Taylor)

We are climbing Jesus' ladder, ladder,
we are climbing Jesus' ladder, ladder,
we are climbing Jesus' ladder, ladder,
children of the Lord.

So let's all
rise and shine and give God the
glory, glory,
rise and shine and give God the
glory, glory,
rise and shine and give God the
glory, glory,
children of the Lord.

We are following where he leads us,
leads us,
we are following where he leads us,
leads us,
we are following where he leads us,
leads us,
children of the Lord.

We are reaching out to others, others,
we are reaching out to others, others,
we are reaching out to others, others,
children of the Lord.

We are one with all who serve him,
serve him,
we are one with all who serve him,
serve him,
we are one with all who serve him,
serve him,
children of the Lord.

121 Traditional South African, trans. Anders Nyberg

We are marching in the light of God. (4)
We are marching,
Oo, we are marching in the light of God.
We are marching,
Oo, we are marching in the light of God.

To create further verses, 'marching' may be replaced with 'dancing', 'singing', 'praying', etc.

122 Michael Forster

We can plough and dig the land,
we can plant and sow,
we can water, we can weed,
but we can't make things grow.

> *That is something only God can do, (3)*
> *only God can make things grow.*

We can edge and we can prune,
we can rake and hoe,
we can lift and we can feed,
but we can't make things grow.

We can watch the little shoots
sprouting row by row,
we can hope and we can pray,
but we can't make things grow.

123 Fred Kaan

We have a King who rides a donkey, (3)
and his name is Jesus.

> *Jesus the King is risen, (3)*
> *early in the morning.*

Trees are waving a royal welcome (3)
for the King called Jesus.

We have a King who cares for people (3)
and his name is Jesus.

A loaf and a cup upon the table, (3)
bread-and-wine is Jesus.

We have a King with a bowl and
   towel, (3)
Servant-King is Jesus.

What shall we do with our life this
   morning? (3)
Give it up in service!

124 Matthias Claudius, trans. Jane Montgomery Campbell, alt.

We plough the fields, and scatter
the good seed on the land,
but it is fed and watered
by God's almighty hand:
he sends the snow in winter,
the warmth to swell the grain,
the breezes and the sunshine,
and soft, refreshing rain.

> *All good gifts around us*
> *are sent from heav'n above;*
> *then thank the Lord, O thank the Lord,*
> *for all his love.*

He only is the maker
of all things near and far;
he paints the wayside flower,
he lights the evening star.
He fills the earth with beauty,
by him the birds are fed;
much more to us, his children,
he gives our daily bread.

Continued overleaf

We thank thee, then, O Father,
for all things bright and good:
the seed-time and the harvest,
our life, our health, our food.
Accept the gifts we offer
for all thy love imparts,
and, what thou most desirest,
our humble, thankful hearts.

All good gifts around us
are sent from heav'n above;
then thank the Lord, O thank the Lord,
for all his love.

125 Jan Struther

When a knight won his spurs, in the
    stories of old,
he was gentle and brave, he was
    gallant and bold;
with a shield on his arm and a lance
    in his hand,
for God and for valour he rode through
    the land.

No charger have I, and no sword by
    my side,
yet still to adventure and battle I ride,
though back into storyland giants
    have fled,
and the knights are no more and the
    dragons are dead.

Let faith be my shield and let joy be
    my steed
'gainst the dragons of anger, the ogres
    of greed;
and let me set free, with the sword of
    my youth,
from the castle of darkness the pow'r
    of the truth.

126 Paul Booth

When God made the garden of creation,
he filled it full of his love;
when God made the garden of creation,
he saw that it was good.
There's room for you, and room for me,
and room for ev'ryone:
for God is a Father who loves his
    children,
and gives them a place in the sun.
When God made the garden of creation,
he filled it full of his love.

When God made the hamper of
    creation,
he filled it full of his love;
when God made the hamper of creation,
he saw that it was good.
There's food for you, and food for me,
and food enough for all:
but often we're greedy, and waste
    God's bounty,
so some don't get any at all.
When God made the hamper of
    creation,
he filled it full of his love.

When God made the fam'ly of creation,
he filled it full of his love;
when God made the fam'ly of creation,
he saw that it was good.
There's love for you, and love for me,
and love for ev'ryone:
but sometimes we're selfish, ignore
    our neighbours,
and seek our own place in the sun.
When God made the fam'ly of creation,
he filled it full of his love.

When God made the garden of creation,
he filled it full of his love;
When God made the garden of creation,
he saw that it was good.
There's room for you,
and room for me,
and room for ev'ryone:
for God is a Father who loves his
    children,
and gives them a place in the sun.
When God made the garden of creation,
he filled it full of his love.

127 Sydney Carter

When I needed a neighbour
were you there, were you there?
When I needed a neighbour,
were you there?

And the creed and the colour
and the name won't matter,
were you there?

I was hungry and thirsty . . .

I was cold, I was naked . . .

When I needed a shelter . . .

When I needed a healer . . .

Wherever you travel
I'll be there, I'll be there,
wherever you travel
I'll be there.

And the creed and the colour
and the name won't matter,
I'll be there.

128 John Glandfield

When Jesus walked in Galilee,
he gave all men a chance to see
what God intended them to be,
and how they ought to live.

When Jesus hung upon the cross,
enduring hunger, pain and loss,
he looked, with loving eyes, across
the scene, and said, 'Forgive.'

When Jesus rose on Easter Day,
he met a woman in the way
and said, 'Go to my friends, and say
the Master is alive.'

When Jesus comes to us each day,
and listens to us as we pray,
we'll listens too, and hear him say,
'Come, follow me, and live!'

129 Ann Conlon

When your Father made the world,
before that world was old,
in his eye what he had made was
    lovely to behold.
Help your people to care for your world.

The world is a garden you made,
and you are the one who planted
    the seed,
the world is a garden you made,
a life for our food, life for our joy,
life we could kill with our selfish greed.

Continued overleaf

All the world that he had made,
the seas, the rocks, the air,
all the creatures and the plants he
    gave into our care.
Help your people to care for your world.

The world is a garden you made,
and you are the one who planted
    the seed,
the world is a garden you made,
a life for our food, life for our joy,
life we could kill with our selfish greed.

When you walked in Galilee,
you said your Father knows
when each tiny sparrow dies, each
    fragile lily grows.
Help your people to care for your world.

And the children of the earth,
like sheep within your fold,
should have food enough to eat, and
    shelter from the cold.
Help your people to care for your world.

130 Paul Booth

Who put the colours in the rainbow?
Who put the salt into the sea?
Who put the cold into the snowflake?
Who made you and me?
Who put the hump upon the camel?
Who put the neck on the giraffe?
Who put the tail upon the monkey?
Who made hyenas laugh?
Who made whales and snails and
    quails?
Who made hogs and dogs and frogs?
Who made bats and rats and cats?
Who made ev'rything?

Who put the gold into the sunshine?
Who put the sparkle in the stars?
Who put the silver in the moonlight?
Who made Earth and Mars?
Who put the scent into the roses?
Who taught the honey bee to dance?
Who put the tree inside the acorn?
It surely can't be chance!
Who made seas and leaves and trees?
Who made snow and winds that blow?
Who made streams and rivers flow?
God made all of these!

131 Unknown

Who's the king of the jungle?
Who's the king of the sea?
Who's the king of the universe,
and who's the king of me?
I'll tell you:
J - E - S - U - S is.
He's the king of me:
he's the king of the universe,
the jungle and the sea.

132 C. Austin Miles

Wide, wide as the ocean, high as the
    heaven above;
deep, deep as the deepest sea is my
    Saviour's love.
I, though so unworthy, still am a child
    of his care;
for his word teaches me that his love
    reaches me everywhere.

133 Pamela Verrall

Would you walk by on the other side,
when someone called for aid?
Would you walk by on the other side,
and would you be afraid?

Cross over the road, my friend,
ask the Lord his strength to lend,
his compassion has no end,
cross over the road.

Would you walk by on the other side,
when you saw a loved one stray?
Would you walk by on the other side,
or would you watch and pray?

Would you walk by on the other side,
when starving children cried?
Would you walk by on the other side
and would you not provide?

© Herald Music Services

134 Geoffrey Gardner

You can build a wall around you,
stone by stone, a solid ring;
you can live alone, in an empty home,
be in charge and be the king.

Break out, reach out,
make the walls crumble down,
down, down.
Break out, reach out,
make the walls tumble down.

You can build a wall around you,
stop the sun from shining in;
there'll be snow-topped trees and a
chilling breeze,
always winter, never spring.

You can build a wall around you,
slam the door shut fast and firm;
there's no friend at hand who can
understand,
to love you, and help you learn.

Based on Oscar Wilde's story *The Selfish Giant*.

© Geoffrey Gardner

135 Stuart Dauermann

You shall go out with joy
and be led forth with peace,
and the mountains and the hills
shall break forth before you.
There'll be shouts of joy,
and the trees of the field
shall clap, shall clap their hands.
And the trees of the field
shall clap their hands,
and the trees of the field
shall clap their hands,
and the trees of the field
shall clap their hands,
and you'll go out with joy.

© 1975 Lillenas Publishing Co./Thankyou Music

Christmas songs and carols

136 William James Kirkpatrick, vv. 2 & 3 adapted by Michael Forster

Away in a manger, no crib for a bed,
the little Lord Jesus laid down his
 sweet head.
The stars in the bright sky looked
 down where he lay,
the little Lord Jesus, asleep on the hay.

The cattle are lowing, they also adore
the little Lord Jesus who lies in the
 straw.
I love you, Lord Jesus, I know you are
 near
to love and protect me, till morning is
 here.

Be near me, Lord Jesus, I ask you to stay
close by me for ever, and love me, I pray.
Bless all the dear children in your
 tender care,
prepare us for heaven, to live with you
 there.

This version © Kevin Mayhew Ltd

137 Geoffrey Ainger

Born in the night, Mary's child,
a long way from your home;
coming in need, Mary's child,
born in a borrowed room.

Clear shining light, Mary's child,
your face lights up our way;
light of the world, Mary's child,
dawn on our darkened day.

Truth of our life, Mary's child,
you tell us God is good;
prove it is true, Mary's child,
go to your cross of wood.

Hope of the world, Mary's child,
you're coming soon to reign;
King of the earth, Mary's child,
walk in our streets again.

© 1964 Stainer & Bell Ltd

138 Valerie Collison

Come and join the celebration.
It's a very special day.
Come and share our jubilation;
there's a new King born today!

See, the shepherds
hurry down to Bethlehem,
gaze in wonder
at the Son of God who lay before them.

Wise men journey,
led to worship by a star,
kneel in homage,
bringing precious gifts from lands afar.
 So:

'God is with us',
round the world the message bring.
He is with us,
'Welcome', all the bells on earth are
 pealing.

© 1972 High-Fye Music Ltd

139 Katherine K. Davis

Come, they told me, pah-rum-pum-
pum-pum!
our new born King to see, pah-rum-
pum-pum-pum!
Our finest gifts we bring, pah-rum-
pum-pum-pum!
to lay before the King, pah-rum-pum-
pum-pum!
Rum-pum-pum-pum! Rum-pum-pum-
pum!
So, to honour him, pah-rum-pum-
pum-pum!
when we come.

Baby Jesus, pah-rum-pum-pum-pum!
I am a poor child too, pah-rum-pum-
pum-pum!
I have no gift to bring, pah-rum-pum-
pum-pum!
that's fit to give a King, pah-rum-pum-
pum-pum!
Rum-pum-pum-pum! Rum-pum-pum-
pum!
Shall I play for you, pah-rum-pum-
pum-pum!
on my drum?

Mary nodded, pah-rum-pum-pum-pum!
The ox and lamb kept time, pah-rum-
pum-pum-pum!
I played my drum for him, pah-rum-
pum-pum-pum!
I played my best for him, pah-rum-
pum-pum-pum!
Rum-pum-pum-pum! Rum-pum-pum-
pum!
Then he smiled at me, pah-rum-pum-
pum-pum!
me and my drum.

140 George Ratcliffe Woodward

Ding dong! merrily on high,
in heav'n the bells are ringing;
ding dong! verily the sky
is riv'n with angels singing.

Gloria, hosanna in excelsis! (2)

E'en so here below, below,
let steeple bells be swungen,
and io, io, io,
by priest and people sungen.

Pray you, dutifully prime
your matin chime, ye ringers;
may you beautifully rhyme
your evetime song, ye singers.

141 M. Sargent

Girls and boys, leave your toys, make
no noise,
kneel at his crib and worship him.
For this shrine, Child divine, is the sign
our Saviour's here.
Alleluia, the church bells ring,
'Alleluia!' the angels sing,
alleluia from everything –
all must draw near!

On that day, far away, Jesus lay –
angels were watching round his head.
Holy Child, mother mild, undefiled,
we sing your praise.
Alleluia, the church bells ring,
'Alleluia!' the angels sing,
alleluia from everything –
our hearts we raise.

Shepherds came at the fame of your
name,
angels their guide to Bethlehem;
in that place saw your face filled with
grace,
stood at your door.
Alleluia, the church bells ring,
'Alleluia!' the angels sing,
alleluia from everything –
love evermore.

142 Spiritual

Go, tell it on the mountain,
over the hills and ev'rywhere.
Go, tell it on the mountain
that Jesus Christ is born.

While shepherds kept their watching
o'er wand'ring flocks by night,
behold, from out of heaven,
there shone a holy light.

And lo, when they had seen it,
they all bowed down and prayed;
they travelled on together
to where the babe was laid.

When first I was a seeker,
I sought both night and day;
I asked the Lord to help me
and he showed me the way.

He set me as a watchman
upon the city wall,
and if I am a Christian,
I am the least of all.

143 Charles Wesley, George Whitefield, Martin Madan and others, alt.

Hark, the herald-angels sing
glory to the new-born King;
peace on earth and mercy mild,
God our sinners reconciled:
joyful, all ye nations rise,
join the triumph of the skies,
with th'angelic host proclaim,
'Christ is born in Bethlehem.'

Hark, the herald-angels sing
glory to the new-born King.

Christ, by highest heav'n adored,
Christ, the everlasting Lord,
late in time behold him come,
offspring of a virgin's womb!
Veiled in flesh the Godhead see,
hail, th'incarnate Deity!
Pleased as man with us to dwell,
Jesus, our Emmanuel.

Hail, the heav'n-born Prince of Peace!
Hail, the Sun of Righteousness!
Light and life to all he brings,
ris'n with healing in his wings;
mild he lays his glory by,
born that we no more may die,
born to raise us from the earth,
born to give us second birth.

144 Michael Forster

Hee, haw! Hee, haw!
Doesn't anybody care?
There's a baby in my dinner
and it's just not fair!

Continued overleaf

Jesus in the manger,
lying in the hay,
far too young to realise he's getting in
the way!
I don't blame the baby,
not his fault at all,
but his parents should respect a
donkey's feeding stall!

Hee, haw! Hee, haw!
Doesn't anybody care?
There's a baby in my dinner
and it's just not fair!

After all that journey,
with my heavy load,
did I ever once complain about the
dreadful road?
I can cope with backache,
and these swollen feet.
All I ask is some respect, and one
square meal to eat.

'Be prepared,' I told them,
'better book ahead.'
Joseph said, 'Don't be an ass,' and
took a chance instead.
Now they've pinched my bedroom,
people are so rude!
I can cope with that, but not a baby in
my food!

145 Sydney Carter

Here we go up to Bethlehem,
Bethlehem, Bethlehem.
Here we go up to Bethlehem
on a cold and frosty morning.

We've got to be counted in Bethlehem,
Bethlehem, Bethlehem.
We've got to be counted in Bethlehem
on a cold and frosty morning.

Where shall we stay in Bethlehem,
Bethlehem, Bethlehem?
Where shall we stay in Bethlehem
on a cold and frosty morning?

146 Christina Rossetti

In the bleak mid-winter
frosty wind made moan,
earth stood hard as iron,
water like a stone;
snow had fallen, snow on snow,
snow on snow,
in the bleak mid-winter, long ago.

Our God, heav'n cannot hold him
nor earth sustain;
heav'n and earth shall flee away
when he comes to reign.
In the bleak mid-winter
a stable place sufficed
the Lord God almighty, Jesus Christ.

Enough for him, whom cherubim
worship night and day,
a breastful of milk,
and a mangerful of hay:
enough for him, whom angels
fall down before,
the ox and ass and camel which adore.

Angels and archangels
may have gathered there,
cherubim and seraphim
thronged the air;
but only his mother
in her maiden bliss
worshipped the beloved with a kiss.

What can I give him,
poor as I am?
If I were a shepherd
I would bring a lamb;
if I were a wise man
I would do my part,
yet what I can I give him: give my heart.

147 Joy Webb

It was on a starry night, when the hills
    were bright.
Earth lay sleeping, sleeping calm and
    still;
then in a cattle shed, in a manger bed,
a boy was born, King of all the world.

And all the angels sang for him
the bells of heaven rang for him;
for a boy was born, King of all the
    world.
And all the angels sang for him,
the bells of heaven rang for him;
for a boy was born, King of all the
    world.

Soon the shepherds came that way,
    where the baby lay,
and were kneeling, kneeling by his side.
And their hearts believed again, for
    the peace of men;
for a boy was born, King of all the
    world.

On a starry night,
on a starry night.

148 Joan Lawton

Kings came riding from the East,
searching for the Prince of peace;
then king Herod, wicked man,
schemed and plotted evil plan.

Herod told them: 'Find the babe;
come and tell me where he's laid:
I will go there, kneel me down,
offer him my golden crown.'

But all he wanted was his blood,
have this infant gone for good.
Quickly riding through the sand,
kings left Herod's desert land.

149 Eric Boswell

Little donkey, little donkey,
on the dusty road,
got to keep on plodding onwards
with your precious load.
Been a long time, little donkey,
through the winter's night;
don't give up now, little donkey,
Bethlehem's in sight.

Ring out those bells tonight,
Bethlehem, Bethlehem,
follow that star tonight,
Bethlehem, Bethlehem.
Little donkey, little donkey,
had a heavy day,
little donkey, carry Mary safely on
    her way.

Continued overleaf

Little donkey, little donkey,
on the dusty road,
there are wise men, waiting for a
sign to bring them here.
Do not falter, little donkey,
there's a star ahead;
it will guide you, little donkey,
to a cattle shed.

Ring out those bells tonight,
Bethlehem, Bethlehem,
follow that star tonight,
Bethlehem, Bethlehem.
Little donkey, little donkey,
had a heavy day,
little donkey, carry Mary safely on
her way.

150 Traditional Czech Carol, translated by Percy Dearmer

Little Jesus, sweetly sleep, do not stir;
we will lend a coat of fur;
we will rock you, rock you, rock you,
we will rock you, rock you, rock you:
see the fur to keep you warm,
snugly round your tiny form.

Mary's little baby sleep, sweetly sleep,
sleep in comfort, slumber deep;
we will rock you, rock you, rock you,
we will rock you, rock you, rock you:
we will serve you all we can,
darling, darling little man.

151 Spiritual, alt.

Mary had a baby, yes, Lord.
Mary had a baby, yes, my Lord.
Mary had a baby, yes, Lord.
And God became a human being just
  like me.

What did she name him?

Mary named him Jesus.

Where was he born?

Born in a stable!

Where did she lay him?

Laid him in a manger,

152 Possibly by John Francis Wade, trans. Frederick Oakeley and others

O come, all ye faithful,
joyful and triumphant,
O come ye, O come ye to Bethlehem.
Come and behold him,
born the King of angels:

O come, let us adore him,
O come, let us adore him,
O come, let us adore him,
Christ the Lord.

God of God,
Light of Light,
lo, he abhors not the virgin's womb;
Very God,
begotten, not created:

Sing, choirs of angels,
sing in exultation,
sing, all ye citizens of heav'n above;
glory to God
in the highest:

Yea, Lord, we greet thee,
born this happy morning,
Jesu, to thee be glory giv'n;
Word of the Father,
now in flesh appearing:

153 Phillips Brooks, alt.

O little town of Bethlehem,
how still we see thee lie!
Above thy deep and dreamless sleep
the silent stars go by.
Yet in thy dark streets shineth
the everlasting light;
the hopes and fears of all the years
are met in thee tonight.

For Christ is born of Mary;
and, gathered all above,
while mortals sleep, the angels keep
their watch of wond'ring love;
O morning stars, together
proclaim the holy birth,
and praises sing to God the King,
and peace upon the earth.

How silently, how silently,
the wondrous gift is giv'n!
So God imparts to human hearts
the blessings of his heav'n.
No ear may hear his coming;
but in this world of sin,
where meek souls will receive him, still
the dear Christ enters in.

O holy child of Bethlehem,
descend to us, we pray;
cast out our sin and enter in,
be born in us today.
We hear the Christmas angels
the great glad tidings tell:
O come to us, abide with us,
our Lord Emmanuel.

154 vv. 1, 2, 3 & 5: Cecil Frances Alexander; v. 4: Michael Forster

Once in royal David's city
stood a lowly cattle shed,
where a mother laid her baby
in a manger for his bed:
Mary was that mother mild,
Jesus Christ her little child.

He came down to earth from heaven,
who is God and Lord of all,
and his shelter was a stable,
and his cradle was a stall;
with the humble, poor and lowly,
lived on earth our Saviour holy.

And through all his wondrous
    childhood,
day by day like us he grew;
he was little, weak and helpless,
tears and smiles like us he knew;
and he feeleth for our sadness,
and he shareth in our gladness.

Still, among the poor and lowly,
hope in Christ is brought to birth,
with the promise of salvation
for the nations of the earth;
still in him our life is found,
and our hope of heav'n is crowned.

Continued overleaf

And our eyes at last shall see him,
through his own redeeming love,
for that child, so dear and gentle,
is our Lord in heav'n above;
and he leads his children on
to the place where he is gone.

v. 4 © Kevin Mayhew Ltd

155 Peggy Blakeley

Rat-a-tat-tat, rat-a-tat-tat.
No! No! No!
There isn't any room
and you can't stay here,
there isn't any room for strangers.
The wind may be chill
and the night may be cold,
and be full of nasty noises in the dark
   and dangers.
But there isn't any room,
there isn't any room,
there isn't any room for strangers.

Rat-a-tat-tat, rat-a-tat-tat.
Yes! Yes! Yes!
There is a little room
and you may stay here,
we have a little place for strangers.
Come in from the night
to the stable so bare
which is full of warmth and
   friendliness and safe from dangers.
Yes, there is a little room,
there is a little room,
there is a little room for strangers.

© A & C Black Publishers Ltd

156 Edward Caswall

See, amid the winter's snow,
born for us on earth below,
see, the tender Lamb appears,
promised from eternal years.

Hail, thou ever blessèd morn,
hail, redemption's happy dawn!
Sing through all Jerusalem,
Christ is born in Bethlehem.

Lo, within a manger lies
he who built the starry skies;
he who, throned in heights sublime,
sits amid the cherubim.

Say, ye holy shepherds, say,
what your joyful news today?
Wherefore have ye left your sheep
on the lonely mountain steep?

'As we watched at dead of night,
lo, we saw a wondrous light;
angels, singing peace on earth,
told us of the Saviour's birth.'

Sacred infant, all divine,
what a tender love was thine,
thus to come from highest bliss,
down to such a world as this!

Virgin mother, Mary, blest,
by the joys that fill thy breast,
pray for us, that we may prove
wothy of the Saviour's love.

157 Michael Perry

See him lying on a bed of straw,
a draughty stable with an open door,
Mary cradling the babe she bore:
the Prince of Glory is his name.

O now carry me to Bethlehem,
to see the Lord of love again:
just as poor as was the stable then,
the Prince of Glory when he came!

Star of silver, sweep across the skies,
show where Jesus in the manger lies;
shepherds, swiftly from your stupor rise
to see the Saviour of the world!

Angels, sing again the song you sang,
sing the story of God's gracious plan,
sing that Bethl'em's little baby can
be the Saviour of us all.

Mine are riches from your poverty;
from your innocence, eternity;
mine, forgiveness by your death for me,
child of sorrow for my joy.

© Mrs B. Perry/Jubilate Hymns

158 Joseph Mohr, trans. John Freeman Young

Silent night, holy night.
All is calm, all is bright,
round yon virgin mother and child,
holy infant, so tender and mild:
sleep in heavenly peace,
sleep in heavenly peace.

Silent night, holy night.
Shepherds quake at the sight,
glories stream from heaven afar,
heav'nly hosts sing alleluia:
Christ the Saviour is born,
Christ the Saviour is born.

Silent night, holy night.
Son of God, love's pure light,
radiance beams from thy holy face,
with the dawn of redeeming grace:
Jesus, Lord, at thy birth,
Jesus, Lord, at thy birth.

159 Sabine Baring-Gould

The angel Gabriel from heaven came,
his wings as drifted snow, his eyes as
    flame.
'All hail,' said he, 'thou lowly maiden,
    Mary,
most highly favoured lady.' Gloria!

'For known a blessèd mother thou
    shalt be.
All generations laud and honour thee.
Thy Son shall be Emmanuel, by seers
    foretold,
most highly favoured lady.' Gloria!

Then gentle Mary meekly bowed her
    head.
'To me be as it pleaseth God,' she said.
'My soul shall laud and magnify his
    holy name.'
Most highly favoured lady. Gloria!

Of her, Emmanuel the Christ was born
in Bethlehem, all on a Christmas morn;
and Christian folk throughout the
    world will ever say:
'Most highly favoured lady.' Gloria!

160 From William Sandys' Christmas Carols Ancient and Modern

The first nowell the angel did say
was to certain poor shepherds in
    fields as they lay;
in fields where they lay, keeping their
    sheep,
on a cold winter's night that was so
    deep.

Nowell, nowell,
nowell, nowell,
born is the King of Israel!

Continued overleaf

They lookèd up and saw a star
shining in the east, beyond them far,
and to the earth it gave great light,
and so it continued both day and night.

Nowell, nowell,
nowell, nowell,
born is the King of Israel!

And by the light of that same star,
three wise men came from country far;
to seek for a king was their intent,
and to follow the star wherever it went.

This star drew nigh to the north-west,
o'er Bethlehem it took its rest,
and there it did both stop and stay
right over the place where Jesus lay.

Then entered in those wise men three,
full rev'rently upon their knee,
and offered there, in his presence,
their gold and myrrh and frankincense.

Then let us all with one accord
sing praises to our heavenly Lord,
that hath made heav'n and earth of
    naught,
and with his blood mankind hath
    bought.

161 Traditional English Carol

The holly and the ivy,
when they are both full grown,
of all the trees that are in the wood,
the holly bears the crown.

The rising of the sun,
and the running of the deer,
the playing of the merry organ,
sweet singing in the choir.

The holly bears a blossom
as white as the lily flow'r,
and Mary bore sweet Jesus Christ
to be our sweet Saviour.

The holly bears a berry
as red as any blood,
and Mary bore sweet Jesus Christ
to do poor sinners good.

The holly bears a prickle
as sharp as any thorn,
and Mary bore sweet Jesus Christ
on Christmas day in the morn.

The holly bears a bark
as bitter as any gall,
and Mary bore sweet Jesus Christ
for to redeem us all.

The holly and the ivy,
when they are both full grown,
of all the trees that are in the wood
the holly bears the crown.

162 Traditional West Indian

The Virgin Mary had a baby boy,
the Virgin Mary had a baby boy,
the Virgin Mary had a baby boy,
and they said that his name was Jesus.

He came from the glory,
he came from the glorious kingdom.
He came from the glory,
he came from the glorious kingdom.
O yes, believer. O yes, believer.
He came from the glory,
he came from the glorious kingdom.

The angels sang when the baby was
    born, (3)
and proclaimed him the Saviour Jesus.

The wise men saw where the baby
    was born, (3)
and they saw that his name was Jesus.

163 John Henry Hopkins

We three kings of Orient are;
bearing gifts we traverse afar;
field and fountain,
moor and mountain,
following yonder star.

O star of wonder, star of night,
star with royal beauty bright;
westward leading, still proceeding,
guide us to thy perfect light.

Born a King on Bethlehem plain,
gold I bring to crown him again,
King for ever, ceasing never
over us all to reign.

Frankincense to offer have I,
Incense owns a Deity nigh,
prayer and praising gladly raising,
worship him, God most high.

Myrrh is mine, its bitter perfume
breathes a life of gathering gloom;
sorrowing, sighing, bleeding, dying,
sealed in the stone-cold tomb.

Glorious now, behold him arise,
King and God and sacrifice;
alleluia, alleluia,
earth to heav'n replies.

164 Traditional English carol

We wish you a merry Christmas, (3)
and a happy new year!

Good tidings we bring
to you and your kin;
we wish you a merry Christmas,
and a happy new year!

Now bring us some figgy pudding, (3)
and bring some out here.

We all like figgy pudding, (3)
so bring some out here.

We won't go until we've got some, (3)
so bring some out here.

165 Arthur Scholey

When the winter day is dying
and the wind is blowing wild,
listen for a lonely crying,
it may be the wandering Child.
    Light a candle in your window
    let the night know that you care.
    Light a candle in the window,
    it may guide the Christ-Child there.

When at times you fear to follow
on the track that you must tread,
friendly promises are hollow
for the tests that lie ahead –
    light a candle in your window
    when your final hope is gone.
    Light a candle in the window,
    and the Child will lead you on.

Continued overleaf

When the world outside is waiting
but you can't give any more –
there's no end to war and hating
and you long to close the door –
    light a candle in your window,
    let it shine beyond your pain.
    Light a candle in the window,
    and the Child will come again.

166 Nahum Tate

While shepherds watched their flocks
    by night,
all seated on the ground,
the angel of the Lord came down,
and glory shone around.

'Fear not,' said he (for mighty dread
had seized their troubled mind);
'glad tidings of great joy I bring
to you and all mankind.

'To you, in David's town this day,
is born, of David's line,
a Saviour who is Christ the Lord;
and this shall be the sign:

'The heav'nly babe you there shall find
to human view displayed,
all meanly wrapped in swathing bands
and in a manger laid.'

Thus spake the seraph, and forthwith
appeared a shining throng
of angels praising God, who thus
addressed their joyful song:

'All glory be to God on high
and to the earth be peace;
goodwill from heav'n to all the world
begin and never cease.'

Index of First Lines and Titles

This index gives the first line of each hymn. If a hymn is known by an alternative title,
this is also given, but indented and in italics.

Acknowledgements

The publishers wish to express their gratitude to the following for permission to include copyright material in this book. Details of copyright owners are given underneath each individual hymn.

A & C Black Publishers Ltd, Howard Road, Eaton Socon, St Neots, Cambridgeshire, PE19 8EZ. All rights reserved. Used by kind permission.

Bucks Music Ltd., Onward House, 11 Uxbridge Street, London, W8 7TQ.

Hazel Charlton, c/o CCL (Europe) Ltd, Chantry House, 22 Upperton Road, Eastbourne, East Sussex, BN21 1BF.

CopyCare Ltd, PO Box 77, Hailsham, East Sussex, BN27 3EF.

J. Curwen & Sons Ltd, 8/9 Frith Street, London, W1D 3JB. All rights reserved.

Daybreak Music Ltd, Silverdale Road, Eastbourne, East Sussex, BN20 7AB. All rights reserved. International copyright secured.

Durham Music Ltd, Onward House, 11 Uxbridge Street, London, W8 7TQ.

Mr Geoffrey Gardner.

Jancis Harvey, 24 Edgeborough Close, Kentford, Newmarket, Suffolk, CB8 8QY. Used by permission.

Herald Music Services, 28 Church Circle, Farnborough, Hants, GU14 6QQ.

David Higham Associates Ltd, 5-8 Lower John Street, Golden Square, London, W1F 9HA.

High-Fye Music Ltd, 8/9 Frith Street, London W1D 3JB. All rights reserved. International copyright secured.

IMP Publications, Griffin House, 161 Hammersmith Road, London, W6 8BS.

Jubilate Hymns, 4 Thorne Park Road, Chelston, Torquay, TQ2 6RX.

Kingsway Communications Ltd, 26-28 Lottbridge Drove, Eastbourne, East Sussex, BN23 6NT.

Mr Peter R. Lewis for 'God made the colours' from *Junior Praise,* HarperCollins, London, and 'Each day is different', from *Harlequin,* A & C Black, London.

Lindsay Music, 23 Hitchin Street, Biggleswade, Beds, SG18 8AX.

McCrimmon Publishing Co. Ltd, 10-12 High Street, Great Wakering, Southend-on-Sea, Essex, SS3 0EQ.

Mr Tom McGuinness.

Make Way Music, PO Box 263, Croydon, Surrey, CR9 5AP. All rights reserved. International copyright secured.

Mr Geoffrey Marshall-Taylor.

Music Sales Ltd, 8/9 Frith Street, London, W1D 3JB. All rights reserved. International copyright secured.

OCP Publications, 5536 NE Hassalo, Portland, Oregon 97213, USA. All rights reserved.

Oxford University Press, Great Clarendon Street, Oxford, OX2 6DP.

Restoration Music Ltd, PO Box 356, Leighton Buzzard, LU7 3WP, UK.

SCM-Canterbury Press Ltd, St Mary's Works, St Mary's Plain, Norwich, Norfolk, NR3 3BH.

Scripture Union, 207-209 Queensway, Bletchley, Milton Keynes, Buckinghamshire, MK2 2EB.

Marion Skelton, c/o CCL (Europe) Ltd, Chantry House, 22 Uperton Road, Eastbourne, East Sussex, BN21 1BF.

Sovereign Music UK, PO Box 356 Leighton Buzzard, LU7 3WP, UK.

SPCK, Holy Trinity Church, Marylebone Road, London, NW1 4DU.

Stainer & Bell Ltd, PO Box 110, Victoria House, 23 Gruneisen Road, London, N3 1DZ.

Universal/MCA Music Publishing Ltd, 77 Fulham Palace Road, London, W6 8JA. Used by permission of Music Sales Ltd.

Josef Weinberger Ltd., 12-14 Mortimer Street, London, W1T 3JJ.

Wild Goose Publications, Iona Community, Savoy House, 140 Sauchiehall Street, Glasgow, G2 3DH.

Also available from

kevin
mayhew

Hymns and songs for Assembly - 8 CDs
These high-quality ready-to-use CDs contain instrumental
backing tracks for the 166 hymns and songs in this book.
See the joy on the children's faces as you play them over the
school PA system or simply through a CD player. And
singing will improve too!

Product code 1490091

No organist? No problem! – General hymns - 7 CDs
140 popular hymns: traditional hymns have an organ
accompaniment, modern hymns are accompanied by music
group instruments.

Product code 1490080

No organist? No problem! – Seasonal hymns - 3 CDs
60 popular seasonal hymns: traditional hymns have an
organ accompaniment, modern hymns are accompanied by
music group instruments.

Product code 1490081

Keep a lookout for some exciting new products in this range available soon!